MISSION
COMMUNICATIONS

The Story of Bell Laboratories

Prescott C. Mabon

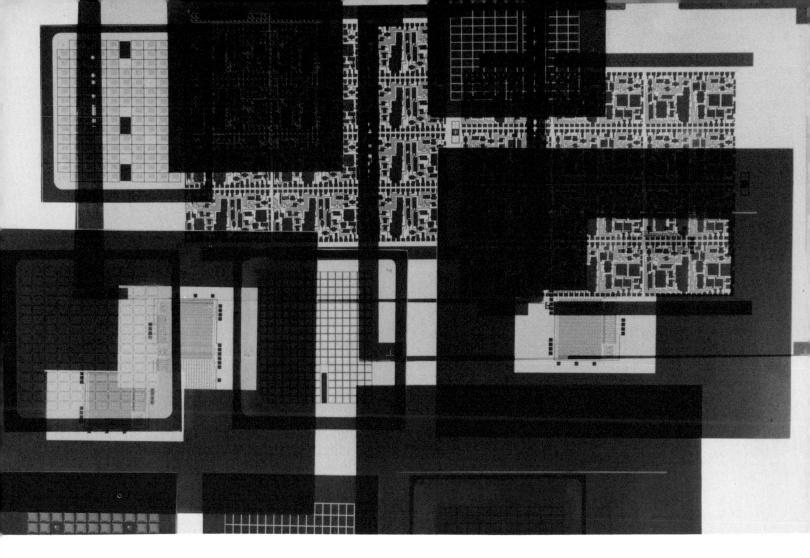

Integrated circuits and the patterns used to manufacture them form an interesting geometric montage. Many such solid-state circuits — small, reliable, economical and low in power consumption — are designed by Bell Laboratories engineers for telephone sets, transmission equipment and switching systems.

CONTENTS

"Our mission at Bell Laboratories, as the title of this book reaffirms, is communications. This is not a temporary mission, as one might think of some expedition or foray. It is Bell Laboratories' life. I see it also as a mission of importance involving great responsibility. Improving communications, more efficient and satisfying handling of information—these I deeply feel are essential to help solve economic and social problems and aid efforts to civilize the future. And while this book largely reviews the past, I hope it will mainly convey that to do our competent share for the future is our absorbing concern."

W. O. Baker

President, Bell Laboratories

PREFACE

During some 30 years at AT&T, I had a persistent interest in Bell Laboratories, where most of the technical innovations introduced into the Bell System have originated. The invitation to renew acquaintance and write this book, therefore, came as a pleasant surprise.

The book sketches some of the salient technical developments in communications, both before and after Bell Laboratories was formally organized 50 years ago. It also comments on changing problems as the ever more sophisticated and potent communications technology has extended its influence on society and, of course, on the Bell System itself. Facts have been checked with individuals at Bell Laboratories, and with others now retired, and I have had a fair number of criticisms and suggestions. However, I suspect my informants and commentators of having leaned over backward to avoid influencing my point of view.

A number of short passages in the book identify individual scientists with pivotal discoveries, developments or areas of study. This seemed a useful even though arbitrary way to cover significant ground. No present member of Bell Laboratories' technical staff has been included in the group, for the simple reason that that kind of selection was just too hard to make.

I appreciate John deButts' interest in providing an introduction. Also, I am especially indebted to Morton D. Fagen of Bell Laboratories for enabling me to obtain and check information with good speed; to Miss R. L. Stumm for typing and retyping; and to those several members of Bell Laboratories who got together the illustrations and tabular material.

P. C. M.

This glowing constellation is formed by pinpoints of light traveling through bundles of tiny glass fibers. In the not-too-distant future, telephone conversations will be carried through such optical fibers, transmitted by light beams.

INTRODUCTION

JOHN D. DEBUTTS
Chairman of the Board
American Telephone and Telegraph Company

In September of 1924, a notice posted on AT&T bulletin boards said that a new organization was about to be formed and would be known "by some such name as Bell Telephone Laboratories."

Sure enough, that was the name when the new company started work in January 1925; and now, surprisingly, Bell Laboratories, our central organization in the Bell System for scientific research and technical development, is fifty years old. I hope a modest celebration of the anniversary will be thought appropriate.

Many people today, I am aware, are apprehensive about science and technology. They see them as the source of processes that reduce opportunities for personal contact, make human beings into "consumers," exhaust natural resources, pollute the environment and pile up unmanageable wastes. A still more gloomy judgment is that our society has come to define progress purely in terms of advances in technology and so has lost its spiritual way.

These ideas are certainly not to be dismissed. It is obvious that the technological revolution alters life-styles and generates profound social and ethical problems as well as physical problems. Yet it is inconceivable that scientific and engineering energies should be stemmed; the challenge to man is to direct them—to lead change rather than be led. Technological advance is neither the measure of progress nor the answer to man's deepest needs. On a more humble plane, however, there is little doubt that most men and women and organizations want communication services and want them to be excellent. Even the stoutest champion of "humanistic" culture will scarcely tolerate a balky phone but will insist, rather, on fast, reliable communications (deeply rooted in technology!) at reasonable cost. These are expectations that Bell Laboratories has in large measure helped to create and must now work hard to satisfy.

MEASURES OF PROGRESS

For nearly a hundred years Bell Laboratories and its predecessor organizations have worked away at the two great problems of electrical communications.

One is to get from here to there. The other—and today more difficult—problem is to connect anyone with anyone else. How these challenges have been attacked is the substance of this book and I shall not try to anticipate. However, as a business manager I may be allowed a few comments on service and cost results and also on the question of financial support of research.

Fifty years ago the average monthly charge for a home telephone was a little over $3.60. This meant that with earnings in manufacturing jobs averaging 64 cents an hour, about 5½ hours of work at that wage were needed to pay the bill.

In 1973, the comparable figures were $7.30 a month for basic home telephone service, and average hourly earnings were $4.06. Hence less than two hours of work were needed to pay the bill.

Fifty years ago also, although one could talk from coast to coast, the charge was $16.50 for three minutes—it took nearly eight minutes on the average to make connections—and on a typical long-distance call one could usually hear about two per cent of the sound level that left the speaker's lips. Today the cost of dialing a call across the country is less than one-tenth as much (and even less than that during more than two-thirds of all the hours in a week), the connection is usually completed in seconds, and there has been a better than 15-fold improvement in what we can call "hearability."*

Now, Bell Laboratories has not been the sole source of these changes. Improvements in manufacture and in operating methods and skills have also been indispensable. Bell System results flow from the joint efforts of people in the regional telephone companies, in Western Electric, our manufacturing organization, in the American Telephone and Tele-

graph Company, and in the Laboratories, and important aspects of this partnership are discussed in this book. Yet the underlying necessity of our technology-based enterprise must be an ever-improving technology, and for this Bell Laboratories and its predecessor organizations have been mainly responsible. Their work underlies the major technical advances in telephone and data communications and their successes in understanding nature have given us access to all unfolding knowledge in the field.

I think it demonstrable that Bell System science and technology have succeeded in making service improvement and economy march along together. The chart below offers one measure of this performance. Another measure of the total job is the number of telephone employees per 10,000 telephones. Fifty years ago this number was 246. Now it is 72. Meanwhile the number of telephones has increased about nine times, many new services have been developed and employment has tripled.

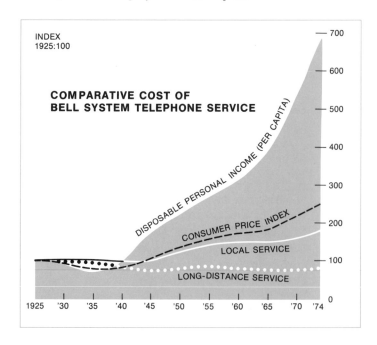

---

*This is a matter not merely of loudness but of faithful reproduction of speech quality.

viii

A DEEPENED RESPONSIBILITY

This is not to suggest that everything has been peaches and cream. Looking at other "network" elements in modern living—rail systems, urban traffic, airways and airports, and so on—I think the communication system most of the time comes off relatively well in terms of cost, speed, dependability and freedom from exasperation. But "relatively well" is hardly a phrase to conjure with. People depend on communications more than in the past and this deepens our responsibility. Also, the margin of tolerance for error is more narrow than it used to be; a spoken word may be understood even though it is not heard clearly, but wrong digits in a data stream can upset a business or confuse the Social Security system, heaven forbid.

We have, therefore, this situation: on the one hand, a much higher level of public expectations, and on the other, a much more complex system with which to satisfy them. No one wants to make anything more difficult than it needs to be, but the inherent technical requirements of a universal system of electrical communications are rather severe. The forces employed are harbored in infinitesimal crystals, on imperceptible films, in subatomic systems that move on command at incomprehensible speeds. And these forces must be precisely organized and balanced in a network that already provides for a possible seven million billion interconnections (in the United States alone) and must provide for billions more in the future as the network continues to grow.

In consequence, we have come to need no lesser technical insights and skills to assure successful operation of complex systems than are required to create those systems in the first place. This lesson was brought home to us—rather too dramatically!— several years ago when near-baffling service problems in several areas demanded for their solution an all-out partnership effort by Bell Laboratories and telephone company people. However, it is not simply to help deal with service emergencies that we rely on our Laboratories partners; it is to help maintain mastery of operations at *all* times.

SUPPORT OF RESEARCH

At the other end of the spectrum of Bell Laboratories' work is basic research, the investigation of nature. And the question is often asked, "Should financial support of research and exploratory development be continuous through thick and thin?" To answer bluntly, our experience tells us, "If at all possible, by all means yes."

For one thing, some work by its nature needs the long view. Work at Bell Laboratories on circular waveguides, for example, capable of carrying hundreds of thousands of conversations simultaneously, has been going on for more than forty years. This has not been a massive effort during all that time, but neither has it faltered. Again, work on lasers and optical transmission systems has proceeded steadily for nearly twenty years. Only now are the needs for waveguide and optical communication systems becoming clear— and the systems will be ready as required.

Let me illustrate further by reference to the depression of the 1930's. In those years the Bell System, like most other businesses, endured hard times and lost a lot of money. Nevertheless it continued to support research. The results justified the decision, for the 1930's proved to be a time of great progress at Bell Laboratories.

The principle of negative feedback, conceived only a short time before, generated a surge of creative work on transmission systems. Bell engineers developed crystal filters that enormously advanced the art of sending many calls over the same channel. They developed the first coaxial cable, and switching systems more capable than any others then in use. Studies in acoustics brought new knowledge of speech and hearing. Work in optics helped prepare us to handle TV programs over communication networks, whenever the day for that might come. Radio research took us a long way toward the modern microwave systems that now carry more than half of the nation's long-distance calls. And experiments with the waveguide, as I have said, proceeded at a modest pace.

Then what happened?

What happened next was World War II. Nearly all work not war-related had to stop—and when Bell Laboratories turned to developing systems for the military, the efforts of the 1930's turned out to be of special value. This was notably true of developments in waveguide systems and high-performance electron tubes. These were essential elements in radar, and soon enough Bell Laboratories became the center of on-the-double programs to develop radar for the armed forces.

The evidence is in fact overwhelming that if Bell System research had wound down during the depression, the results would have been bad on every count. Ability to help in the war effort would have been reduced; and the System would have entered the postwar period, when pent-up demand for telephone service was suddenly loosed, far less able to respond to accelerating need.

THE FUTURE

The president of Bell Laboratories, Dr. William O. Baker, has said, "I believe that the meeting of human needs and national goals through science and engineering is at a very early stage."

In communications, it seems to me, there is much to support this view. For it does appear that the practical possibilities of new systems under development or in sight far exceed the capabilities of what we have in general use today. Just as important, we now have the chance to apply new potentials more effectively than could have been done only a few years ago. To say it differently, we not only have a wealth of new knowledge applicable to communications; we also have better tools today—computer systems—to help pick winners and put them where they are needed.

In sum, we have better means for making better choices. And I am persuaded that our increasingly powerful communications technology, combined with an equal power of thought to bring about its optimum use, with the help of computer systems, will have profound and good consequences. No people anywhere, I believe, have a better realization that the computer is a goad to thinking, not a prop, than the people of Bell Laboratories; and no group, so far as I can see, has been more responsive.

We are now at a new threshold. The central theme of insight and innovation in electronics during the midcentury years and after, it has been said, has been the understanding and sophisticated use of materials. Must not the complementary theme, at least, of innovation in the years ahead center on better organization of everything we learn?

Many think so. And I believe the challenge implied is no less exciting, and may well be more so, than any that Bell Laboratories has confronted in the past. For this is really a reflection, in our business, of the challenges the nation and the world face in dealing with the consequences of technology.

Bell Laboratories in Murray Hill, N.J., corporate headquarters and site of most of the Laboratories' basic research
activities. There are other major locations at Whippany
and Holmdel, N.J., and at Naperville, Ill. In all, there
are 17 Laboratories locations in nine states.

Leading scientists from all over the world visited Western Electric's Engineering Department, predecessor of Bell Laboratories. Here, in 1923, British Nobel prize physicist Sir J. J. Thomson discusses the new 10 kW water-cooled power vacuum tube with F. B. Jewett, who later became the Laboratories' first president. The tube resulted from the invention of the copper-glass seal by the Engineering Department's W. G. Houskeeper. It made possible high-power radio broadcasting and overseas telephony.

WHAT BELL LABORATORIES IS –
AND WHY AND HOW

1

Telephony is now almost a hundred years old, Bell Laboratories only fifty. When we begin with the Laboratories' beginnings, therefore, we are already in the middle of telephone history and in the midst of developing communications technology.

How did things stand fifty years ago? The arts of telephony had already made remarkable progress. Some 15 million Bell telephones were in use in the United States, and long-distance lines interconnected cities and towns in all parts of the country, although by today's standards this service was slow, costly and of mediocre quality. The fact was that research and development conducted by the AT&T Company, and in the Engineering Department of Western Electric, AT&T's manufacturing subsidiary, had led to a nationwide service well beyond the attainment of any other country.*

Why then was Bell Laboratories set up as a separate entity to conduct research and development? What was the big idea?

Documents of the time give various reasons, but underlying them all was this: The new organization, owned jointly by AT&T and Western Electric, would make the Bell System's commitment to sustained research and development clearly visible. The first vital step had been taken years earlier when Theodore N. Vail, president of AT&T, and John J. Carty, the company's chief engineer, determined that a central R&D organization within the Bell System was essential. The logical next step was to give this organization its own unmistakable identity.

Here is a contemporary opinion offered by a Bell Laboratories engineer of wide experience and marked accomplishment: "The decision to have a separate organization," he commented, "was a brilliant one because we are the people who have the mission and the muscle (meaning the technical muscle) to consider both the needs of the operating telephone companies and the need of Western Electric, as manufacturer, to produce in the most effective way the things that we develop."

A UNIQUE SETUP

That puts the matter well. Bell Laboratories people have been positioned in a way that encourages them

---

*The work of earlier years is reviewed in Chapter 2 and in notes about individuals who played significant roles.

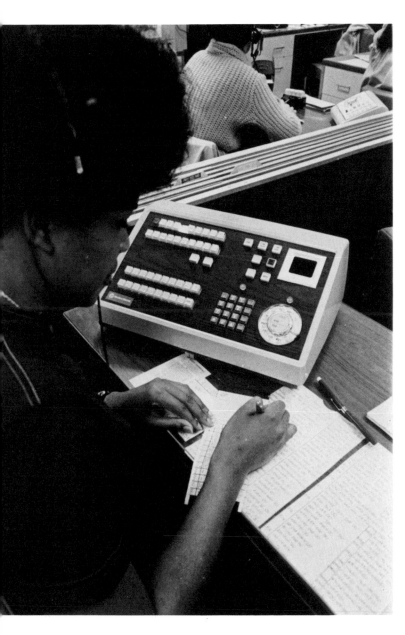

A telephone company employee uses the console of a system developed at Bell Laboratories to check a customer's report of telephone trouble. The system quickly tests the line and the console shows at once what the trouble is.

to understand both the needs of the user (i.e., the telephone companies and their customers) and the need of the maker to produce as well as possible what the user wants. This is an ideal and it is not always fully realized; no one always does everything right. But the setup—which is in fact unique in U.S. industry—has a nice logic. The Laboratories organization is "in the middle" in a good sense, able to reach toward, communicate with, and respond to both producer and consumer.

As time has gone on, the value of this arrangement appears to have increased. The need for teamwork between Bell Laboratories and Western Electric, one may judge, has intensified as the subtleties of development, design and manufacture have become more closely joined. The introduction of a new integrated circuit, for example, depends on the manufacturing process (which itself must be invented) in a way that makes it hard to say just when the circuit designer stops and the maker takes over. When this almost imperceptible transition from design to production involves many new components, all of them to be assembled and assimilated on schedule in a new system, it is quite clear that teamwork is of the essence.

This has been eminently the case, for instance, with the introduction of new electronic switching systems, which rely on countless numbers of new and still-developing solid-state devices in vast arrays and new configurations. To get these systems going, both Bell Laboratories and Western Electric engineers insist, there simply has to be a continuous horizontal flow and feedback of information through all stages of development, design, manufacture and installation. This has been essential to iron out problems, improve designs, control costs and meet schedules. Moreover, the continuing process of improving all systems and equipment means that the information flow must continue over time, from the cradle to the grave of the equipment, so to speak.

H. W. Bode, formerly a vice president of Bell Laboratories and later Gordon McKay Professor of Systems Engineering at Harvard, defined the need in his book, *Synergy,* published by the Laboratories in 1971.

"Continuity in time," Bode wrote, "from project to project, building on the experience and the techniques and skills acquired in the development of the preceding technology, is as vital as collaboration horizontally between development and manufacturing engineers, and it is both of these continuities that are provided and harnessed to Bell System objectives through the integration of research, development and manufacture." To which he added, "The more substantial the step to be taken and the more one is willing to draw on advanced technology, the more important it is that a tight informal association among all the working groups be maintained."

The last point, by the way, seems especially pertinent in view of the fact that we are not many years away from the time when expanding needs for communication will require still another new technology; i.e., the systematic production, transmission, modulation and interconnection of information-bearing waves of light.

NEW DIRECTIONS

There is another reason why the value of Bell Laboratories' positioning in the Bell System may be said to have increased with time. The skills of experts have become more urgently needed to help assure the dependable functioning of the Bell System network, which has become, without much doubt, the most intricate interrelated complex of sensitive devices and systems to be found anywhere in the world. This is discussed more fully in Chapter 9 of this book, but merits a comment here.

Says one Bell Laboratories engineer, "For a long time we were mainly concerned with what we designed and how we might come up with the best hardware at the right price. Now our main concern is—how well are we using what we have?" Another, having in mind no doubt the intense competition that has developed in the communication services, says, "The main question for us is not what technology we should use but how we want to do business." A third says, "I see the Laboratories becoming much more a service organization and for this I am glad."

Remarks like these indicate a significant change in emphasis in recent years. However, they should not obscure the fact that Bell Laboratories' orchestration, if we may call it that, still runs all the way back from operations through design and development to basic research. Hence every possible problem in R&D management presents itself.

PEOPLE . . . PURPOSE . . . ENVIRONMENT

Dr. James B. Fisk, who headed Bell Laboratories from 1959 until his retirement early in 1974, used to sum up his view of the requirements for success in three words: people, purpose and environment. To paraphrase here what he and other Laboratories managers have repeatedly emphasized, one may put the prescription about like this:

The best science and technology will only result from bringing and holding together the best minds. This is the essential reason why Bell Laboratories has done outstanding work. But to bring and hold such minds together takes a lot of doing. They must be located, attracted and challenged. The purpose of the place must be broad enough to give them room and its management wise enough to give them freedom. The free play of creative minds is necessary to the individuals themselves, to the atmosphere they find stimulating, and to their achievement in the interest of the business.

The defined purpose of Bell Laboratories is to do everything it can to advance the arts of communication and assure and improve the technical future of the Bell System. This is sufficiently broad to attract talented people who are mainly or exclusively interested in fundamental studies and investigation. Happily also, this purpose is practical enough to engage the interests of no less able people who most enjoy putting knowledge to use.

Dr. William O. Baker, now president of Bell Laboratories and himself a scientist, has more than once pointed out that the fundamental drive among top-caliber people is their own concept—not the Bell System's concept—of the importance of their work. A scientist's loyalty to his own community in the world of science, Baker reminds us, is as strong as any loyalty to his employer and may be much stronger. But even for the scientist whose main allegiance is not to the business, there is considerable attraction in the combination of broad purpose, real freedom, the proximity of other talented people, ungrudging provision of the tools he needs, and the existence of a structure—the Bell System—in a position to make good use of promising discoveries.

One may venture also that the unabashed conviction of the leaders of Bell Laboratories that science is no less good because it may turn out to be useful has had some influence—not to mention the fact that more than a few scientists who have pursued their goals with success at Bell Laboratories have come to eminence.

LEARNING HOW AND WHY

For many years Bell System research and development were largely empirical, a process of "cut and try." If one material or method did not work, try another—that was the approach. Later, however, it became evident that it was necessary to learn not only whether something would work, but how and why. Innovation came to be seen as the result not of invention alone, but of understanding and what

The basic requirement on Bell Laboratories' management is to attract top-caliber people and confront them with challenging problems. Here mathematician Henry Pollak works surrounded by the books, journals and computer printouts he uses in research.

President Baker has termed evolutionary insight. This has been, in fact, the cornerstone, foundation, call it what you will, of the Bell System's technical achievement. It is the root reason why a relay can operate a billion times, why thousands of voices can travel the same conductor path, and why an amplifier one can hold in two hands can do a better job than a whole roomful of amplifiers could do before.

This is also how the semiconductor revolution came to pass. Twenty years ago an article by Ralph Bown, then Bell Laboratories' vice president for research, summarized the basis for confidence that invention of the transistor at the Laboratories heralded a new era in electronics:

"Industry," Bown wrote, "has spent many millions of dollars during the past three or four years on research, development and pilot manufacture of a new and almost untried device. The actual operating usage to date is almost negligible.* This phenomenal buildup has occurred because the research scientists have understood the new thing with which they are dealing. The development and manufacturing engineers could meet their problems with the confidence of accurate knowledge. And the businessmen have had faith that the scientists and engineers really knew what they are talking about. It seems to me that this is the combination it takes to accomplish the true mission of industrial research."

DEMANDS ARE SEVERE

Dr. Baker has also made clear that the demands of work pursued at Bell Laboratories are no less severe than in what he has termed "the pure discovery culture." Talking to new members of the technical staff not long ago, he observed, "We are trying to find paths in nature, in science, in understanding, which will involve the deepest intellectual insight and

*The first commercial use of transistors in the Bell System was in 1953.

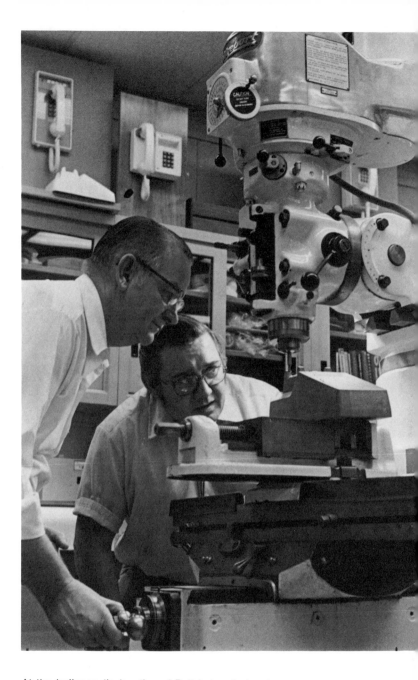

At the Indianapolis location of Bell Laboratories, two employees experiment with techniques for forming a model of a new telephone housing. Bell Laboratories and Western Electric people work together in the Indianapolis building to design and manufacture a wide variety of telephone equipment for homes and offices.

Since 1925 Bell Laboratories scientists and engineers have literally "written the book" in many branches of knowledge associated with their field of telecommunications. Shown here is a partial collection of these works.

importance.* And he added, "The principle is the significant one that we think this community is capable of that kind of scientific exercise."

It is important to note also, however, that the talents and responsibilities of development and systems engineers are not considered of lesser consequence than those of research scientists. Quite the contrary, for three main reasons. One is that scientists must naturally hope that if their work is to be used it will be well used. Second, management, rather obviously, hopes so too! Third, the interaction between scientists and development people is often very stimulating in both directions, not just one.

"By setting scientific standards for development personnel that are just as demanding as those required for research," Dr. Fisk wrote some years ago, "and by requiring equally full understanding of the scientific method, and by providing every opportunity for association and free information flow, we have been able to establish an intimate tie and mutual respect that bridge organizational lines. And we find that this arrangement, far from interfering with research freedom, is welcomed by the researcher—first as an assurance that the development organization will generally be competent to solve its own problems and second, as a guarantee to the researcher that his findings will be exploited where applicable—a satisfaction that even the purest of the pure will admit to."

THORNS AMONG THE ROSES

Bell Laboratories managers are frank to say that not every undertaking works out just as planned. They freely acknowledge, for example, that they have

skill, and at the same time join that with the most concrete utility and value to man. . . . We expect to pursue, as we have, the most elusive and challenging search for the understanding of nature and we expect this to perform, as it has, in the most practical and direct ways of value to our development engineering components and our systems innovation."

In the same talk he suggested that in some future record, several achievements at Bell Laboratories may take their place among discoveries of historic

*Those he referred to were: demonstration of the wave nature of electrons; the principle of negative feedback; information theory; the revelation of what was to become the science of radio astronomy; the first rapid binary calculations; and what he termed, "the whole zone of solid-state molecular and atomic energetics."

sometimes underestimated technical difficulties and cost problems. Take as an instance what might be called the case of the hybrid integrated circuit. These circuits designed at the Laboratories represent a real *tour de force* and today, used in tremendous numbers, they bring advantages in reliability and cost otherwise quite beyond reach. But it took far longer to learn to produce them at favorable cost than had been anticipated, and the same has been true of other elements of the "new" technology.

This is more vexation than failure, perhaps. Nor could one describe as a failure the installation of more than 640 electronic switching systems in the past nine years to serve 11 million customers. Yet Bell Laboratories people readily confess that in their original planning they underestimated the difficulties inherent in programming these computer-like machines to respond exactly right in every conceivable situation when people started to use them. It was only by actually putting the new system into operation and letting it cope with real traffic that all the program wrinkles could be smoothed out— a process that could never have taken place in the development laboratory.

Other difficulties? Well, Picturephone® service, remarkable as it was and is, proved to be ahead of its time when introduced in 1970. An all-embracing communication system once requested by the military had to be acknowledged by all concerned as trying to embrace too much. And years ago, in the first flush of enthusiasm to apply computers to internal Bell System operations, Bell Laboratories launched a program that came near putting the System into the general-purpose computer business, where it assuredly did not belong.* Accordingly, the undertaking was called off, yielding to projects that use the computer manufacturers' hardware.

These are examples, be it noted, of enterprise that runs into problems precisely because it is venturing on new paths. And this very absorption in what is new may sometimes need tempering. A good many Bell Laboratories people agree, for instance, that, when the telephone companies encountered severe service problems in the late 1960's, Laboratories specialists could well have pitched in sooner to help untangle the snarls. Says one executive, "In our preoccupation with the marvelous new things growing out of the transistor, we became partially disengaged from the headaches of operating the network in the face of surging demand, rapid changes in the tempo

In a library at Bell Laboratories, employees use machines that enlarge and display filmed pages for convenient reading and that print paper copies of pages needed for further use. Research and development in telecommunications technology require massive amounts of technical and nontechnical information — reports, computer documentation, government publications, technical journals — which the library system must make readily available.

*Electronic central offices, while using stored programs, are special-purpose systems for interconnecting communications customers and are not general-purpose computers.

and character of communications traffic, mysterious behavior in parts of the network that for a time defied analysis, and urban problems that accentuate employment and training difficulties."

Research programs and new equipment at Bell Laboratories frequently require special parts and devices. To have them made, engineers turn to skilled craftspeople in Laboratories' model shops. Here a glassblower fashions a piece of apparatus for materials research.

A MATTER OF MANAGEMENT

Notwithstanding such comment, Bell Laboratories' success across a wide spectrum of work (now wider than ever by reason of deepening involvement in Bell System operations) is generally considered outstanding. The main reason for this must be—has to be—the quality of the management; and when one looks beyond Dr. Fisk's broad recipe of "people, purpose and environment," it is not hard to find specific indicators. Here are some of them:

Since human talent is the heart of the matter, Bell Laboratories management really goes all out to find and draw the best. Recruiting is not left to a small staff of specialists. Hundreds of the most able technical people in the organization take part. Each spends a few days visiting, year after year, certain departments at one or two universities. In total, some 400 recruiters visit 200 or more institutions annually. Long-term relationships of mutual understanding are developed. When candidates are recommended, interests and opportunities are explored at length. People considering, and considered for, employment usually come to the Laboratories to meet and talk with individuals with whom they may be working. Interviews proceed over days rather than hours.

Going on from there, educational programs undertake to strengthen technical abilities and also to help understanding of Bell Laboratories' overall work and purposes. At so-called "INTRO" programs younger staff members come together to hear Laboratories leaders and other Bell System managers talk about activities and goals; to ask questions and get answers. Departments and groups hold "depth meetings" to let others know what they are doing and why. Formal and informal courses and seminars help people keep abreast of new technical developments. Outstanding university faculty members and young scientists come for limited-term employment.

An extremely liberal publication policy—that is, encouragement of publication to the furthest extent possible consistent with patent protection—also helps to stimulate creative work. In a typical recent year Bell Laboratories scientists and engineers submitted more than 2000 papers for publication in scientific and technical journals and made some 1500 presentations at meetings of professional societies. The Laboratories' own publications include the authoritative *Bell System Technical Journal* and hundreds of papers, monographs and books that are classic in the literature of communications science and technology.

Other indicators of management alertness have to do with the evolution of organizational structure.

For instance, over the years management has moved to bring Bell Laboratories development engineers and designers into closer working association with Western Electric people at manufacturing locations—without, however, loss of their identity or diminution of their development-design function. Similarly, internships and other arrangements are pointed toward bringing Laboratories and telephone company people into the closest possible cooperation.

Another important step was the concept and formation of "fundamental development" groups, working in areas intermediate between basic research and the development of specific instrumentalities or systems. Such fundamental or exploratory development, as it is sometimes called, was vitally important in bringing the promise of the transistor to practical realization and is equally essential today—for instance, in exploring the potentials for optical communication.

Third, we may mention the organization of systems engineering—a practice or discipline that originated by reason of Bell System necessities and has ever since been the object of scrutiny and experiment. The present organization of systems engineering at Bell Laboratories is in fact quite different from that of five years ago. Which is better?

Or will some other arrangement prove better still? Time and experience will tell. The point here is simply that management is in motion to search out opportunities for improvement. Thus it is also that in recent years management has reshaped organization structures specifically to strengthen attack on

Members of a scientific delegation from the People's Republic of China are welcomed as they arrive at Bell Laboratories in Holmdel, N.J. Technical exchanges occur regularly between Bell Laboratories scientists and those from other domestic and foreign companies to discuss mutual interests in science and technology. Also, groups from educational and scientific organizations often visit the Laboratories. In all, about 12,000 visitors come to the Laboratories each year, 9000 of them for technical exchanges.

problems of plant design and operation in the local telephone exchange; on the whole range of techniques for interconnecting system elements, from the microscopic jointures of integrated circuits to cabling assemblies in central offices; and on the application of computer techniques to network operation and maintenance.

Still other important aspects of Bell Laboratories management may be seen in staff services that support the research and development effort. Chapter 11 touches on several of these but we shall mention one here as an illustration. This is the design of buildings to help improve performance.

Bell Laboratories' first building, in New York City, was a conventional structure that had previously housed Western Electric's Engineering Department. The building completed at Murray Hill, New Jersey, however, in 1941 reflected a radically new approach.

Designed on the modular concept, it provided complete flexibility in laboratory arrangements. Partitions on 6-foot modules could be easily moved and 14 necessary services—gases under pressure, water, drains, heat, power—all were available at 6-foot intervals in the outer wall. (Some idea of the dynamics of change at Murray Hill is suggested by the fact that on the average each partition has been moved every seven years; in effect, a new laboratory configuration has been created every seven years within the existing framework.)

Bell Laboratories employees arrive for work at the combined Western Electric—Bell Laboratories location in Atlanta. Producing cable and wire products for the Bell System, Atlanta is one of several locations where close cooperation between Laboratories design groups and Western Electric manufacturing organizations expedites new developments.

Thus a generation ago the first Murray Hill building revolutionized laboratory design. The next major innovation found expression in the Holmdel, New Jersey, building erected in the early 1960's. Here an entirely new kind of plan, evolved by the designers with architect Eero Saarinen, put all laboratories and offices in interior space on short cross-corridors; increased privacy by relegating the main foot traffic to peripheral walkways; located services every 4 feet; and made it even easier to redistribute space.

Tastes differ and some people may find Bell Laboratories buildings austere or even chilly. There is little question, however, that the ideas they reflect have been much in the interest of efficient operation and have strongly influenced laboratory design all over the world.

Generally, one may reflect that significant improvements in technology do not all come out of test tubes or exclusively out of the minds of scientists and

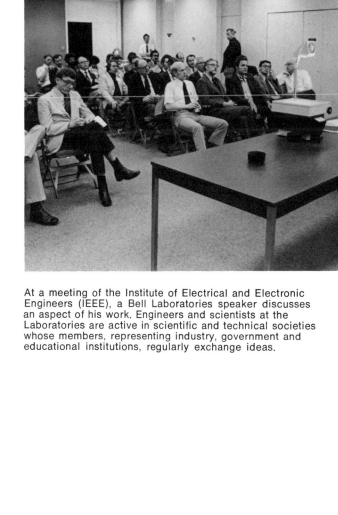

At a meeting of the Institute of Electrical and Electronic Engineers (IEEE), a Bell Laboratories speaker discusses an aspect of his work. Engineers and scientists at the Laboratories are active in scientific and technical societies whose members, representing industry, government and educational institutions, regularly exchange ideas.

Lunchtime provides a chance for relaxation at Bell Laboratories in Indian Hill, Illinois. Indian Hill is the center of electronic switching systems development. Applying the advantages of solid-state electronics to the complexity of telephone switching was—and is—the largest sustained development effort toward a single goal ever undertaken by the Bell System.

engineers. They are also the product of administrative insight and experiment. The very establishment of Bell Laboratories half a century ago bears witness to this. In the beginning, here was a new institution that embodied a new idea conceived by business managers and administrators. And in the years that have followed, the continuing productiveness of the institution has depended on the ability of later administrators to refresh and renew its vitality.

A COMMUNICATING WORLD

In the fifty years since Bell Laboratories was formed, near-instant communications have become truly universal. There are now 116 million Bell and 25 million non-Bell telephones in the United States and more than 198 million in the rest of the world. The Bell System alone operates over 16,000 central offices, 1200 long-distance switching machines, and millions of intercity and interoffice trunk lines. Americans make 516 million calls a day and more than 9.5 billion long-distance calls a year. Not only voices but uncountable quantities of data travel the lines. Special networks woven in and out of the total system serve businesses of every kind, TV and radio stations, defense commands, stock and commodity markets, and federal, state and municipal governments.

Cable and satellite systems link continents. Computers on earth count pulses from space vehicles sliding past other planets. While people sleep, machines turn themselves on to talk with other machines. Men in Chicago get copies of drawings made by men in New York. As the patient's heart beats, the specialist miles away diagnoses his condition. Teachers in Jonestown lecture classes in Smithville and the more vocal students talk back. Computers in the suburbs calculate deposits, withdrawals and interest for millions of depositors in thousands of banks. Ships, barges, aircraft and trucks speak and are heard.

To this communicating world Bell Laboratories, as already suggested, has made outstanding contributions, a fair number of which are presented in other sections of this book. Such accomplishment has not been especially by reason of the Laboratories' size. This is indeed a large organization, and there is no doubt that ability to concentrate many minds on big tough problems has been of great value. However, mere size is no answer in itself and cannot be the simple cause of success. It should be remarked also that the technical staff here represents only 1.6 per cent of all the scientists and engineers at work in industrial research in this country, and expenditures are about 1.9 per cent of what the nation spends for research and development. Whatever successes Bell Laboratories has realized have come not from size alone but from the melding—by management—of all three of the essentials named by Dr. Fisk: people, purpose and environment. As we look ahead, it seems certain that the same factors will be needed to justify the view President Baker has put into three words: "Do not underexpect."

This exhibit of the Bell System network at Bell Laboratories headquarters in Murray Hill, N.J., is designed to show visitors the scope, variety, complexity and flexibility of the telecommunications network operated by the Bell System. It is the Laboratories' mission to do the basic research, development and design, and systems engineering for this vast system.

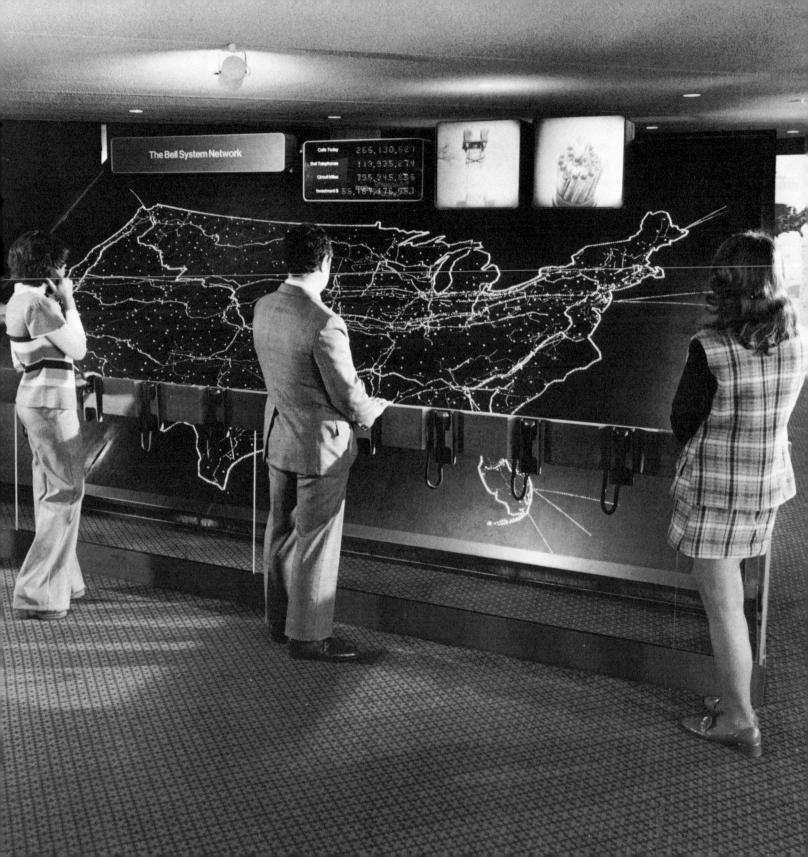

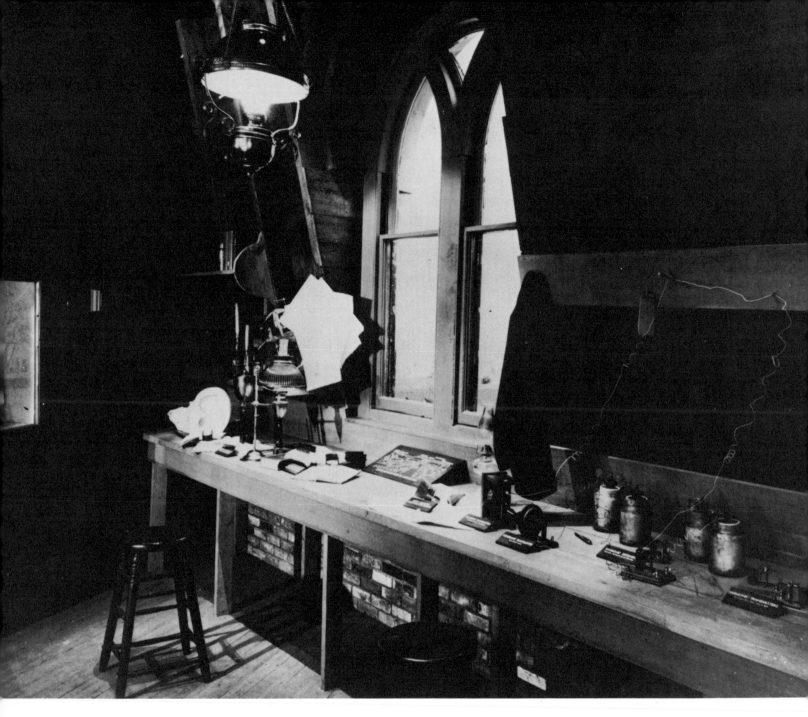

Alexander Graham Bell's original laboratory at 109 Court Street, Boston, Mass., has been recreated by the New England Telephone Company to appear as it did in 1875. This lab might be considered the precursor to the modern Bell Laboratories.

BEGINNINGS TOWARD A DISTANT GOAL 2

In the summer of 1877 Alexander Graham Bell wrote, "I believe, in the future, wires will unite the head offices of the Telephone Company in different cities, and a man in one part of the country may communicate by word of mouth with another in a distant place." He continued (addressing himself to a group of businessmen), "I will impress upon you all the advisability of keeping this end in view, that all present arrangements of the telephone may be eventually realized in this grand system."

Mr. Bell made this remarkable forecast hardly more than two years after the twang of a metal reed, coming over a wire from another room in his attic laboratory in Boston, had verified his concept of a sound-shaped electrical current. His vision was prophetic. Perhaps it was strengthened, in some measure, by a happy underestimate of the difficulties ahead.

FROM THE GROUND UP

For telephony had to make its own way, all the way. In the 1870's there was no profession of electrical engineering, no electric light, and essentially no distribution of electric power. There were no trolley cars. On city streets as on country lanes, horses did all the pulling. Sir William Thomson, who was to become Lord Kelvin, had worked out a theory that explained why telegraph pulses became weakened and distorted as they proceeded along a cable.

Transmission of the human voice, however, was a different matter. Some of the first problems encountered have been well discussed by W. H. Doherty, a student of the past as well as a distinguished development engineer during more than 40 years at Bell Laboratories.

"For one thing," Doherty reminded readers in a 1968 article, "the energy generated by a telephone transmitter was infinitesimal compared with what could be generated by pounding a telegraph key. But more than this, the voice spectrum extended into the hundreds, even thousands, of cycles per second. No one knew how far it had to extend for good intelligibility. As the early practitioners, known as electricians, struggled to coax telegraph wires to carry the voice over longer distances, they were increasingly frustrated and baffled.

"They did not know, for instance, about skin effect,* which in an iron wire is very substantial even at voice frequencies. Thus, they could not understand why the voice died out much faster than the dc resistance of iron had led them to expect, requiring them to resort to copper conductors for the longer distances, and large expensive conductors at that, to keep the resistance low. They were beset by 'earthy' problems: getting reliable connections,

---

*The tendency of a varying current to concentrate in the outer layer of a conductor, with resultant increased resistance.

overcoming electrical interference. When they tried to put wires underground in cables to get around the great congestion on poles and the susceptibility to storm damage, they could not understand why the transmission got so much worse, and especially why the voice became muffled and indistinct in addition to getting weaker."

To put it mildly, there was an immense amount to learn. Several inventors, using "cut and try" methods for the most part, produced telephones that markedly improved the quality and loudness of speech in comparison with what Mr. Bell's original instrument could accomplish. In Connecticut a man named Thomas B. Doolittle found out how to make "hard-drawn" copper wire that would not sag on the spans between poles. Another step forward was to use two-wire metallic circuits instead of a single wire with ground return; this helped to reduce, although it did not eliminate, unwanted noises on the line. To get rid of overhead wires on city streets and put them underground (with the attendant frustrations Doherty has described above), the telephone men first placed the wires in pipes and sealed them against moisture with oil, paraffin or asphaltum. Then they learned to extrude a sheath of lead over a core of conducting wires; to twist pairs of wire together in order to reduce "crosstalk" among the different pairs; to insulate each pair with a wrapping of dry paper . . . .

AN EARLY GIANT STEP

Still, it was a struggle. Progress was slow. Gradually it became understood that telephony, to succeed, required thorough analysis, deeper insights, fundamental understanding. About 1890, studies by the English scientist Oliver Heaviside and others showed that it ought to be possible to make telephone lines more efficient by artificially increasing their inductance. Could this be done by "loading" the lines at intervals with low-resistance coils? In 1899

Engineers — at first known as "electricians" — in the American Bell Telephone Company's Boston Laboratory in 1888. This laboratory marked an early stage in the evolution that led to the creation of Bell Laboratories.

Dr. George A. Campbell, a mathematician who had joined the staff of AT&T two years before, and Professor Michael I. Pupin of Columbia, working independently, found that the key to the problem was the spacing of the coils, and Campbell's formulas for their design and spacing were quickly applied to the construction of loaded lines. With this achievement telephone transmission took a giant step; the voice could now travel twice as far on open-wire pole lines and three or four times as far as had previously been possible over pairs of wire in cables.

By 1892 it had become possible to connect the East with Chicago over lines of heavy open wires strung on poles. In 1911 a loaded open-wire line, using wires almost as thick as rods, could carry the voice

continued on page 19

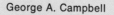

George A. Campbell

First Among His Generation

"The achievements of George Campbell," President F. B. Jewett of Bell Laboratories wrote in 1935, "entitle him beyond question to rank first among his generation of theoretical workers in electrical communication."*

The work most often associated with Campbell's name is, of course, the theory of telephone loading coils and the formulation of rules for their design and spacing (see page 16). He did this work around the turn of the century. It vastly increased the range and efficiency of telephone cable and wire lines and presented the most important single advance in the art of transmission until the development of the high-vacuum tube nearly 15 years later.

With the introduction of vacuum-tube repeaters, loading generally ceased to be applied on long-distance lines. It is still used, however, three-quarters of a century later, on many local cables and especially on those local trunk circuits that handle only voice frequencies.

Loading theory was far from being Campbell's only contribution to telephony. The development of "anti-sidetone" circuits, which minimize the extent to which a person talking on the telephone

---

*Quoted from a memoir by Jewett in the *Bell System Technical Journal,* Vol. XIV, No. 4 (October, 1935), pp. 553-557, at the time of Campbell's retirement from Bell Laboratories.

can hear, in his receiver, tones generated by his own voice, began with him. Campbell also analyzed the problem of crosstalk between circuits and made suggestions that led to new methods for testing telephone cables during their manufacture and installation. He studied the problem of "singing" (or instability) in repeaters and repeatered lines, indicated measures to prevent it, and originated the idea of using four-wire circuits (two wires for each direction of transmission) to improve the performance of long-distance cable systems.

Still, these contributions have been less widely noted than what might fairly be called Campbell's second historic achievement, invention of the electrical wave filter. This made it possible and practical to separate the currents of different frequencies traveling the same transmission path, and thus to handle several (and later many) conversations simultaneously. The patent was issued to Campbell in 1917. By the time Jewett wrote his memoir in 1935 the filter had become, he remarked, "almost as ubiquitous as the vacuum tube."

A further point here: Since loading is much less prevalent than it used to be, and the simultaneous transmission of many communications much more so, it might be thought that Campbell's second great accomplishment was more important than the first. However, as Jewett also pointed out, "The fundamental conception of the electric wave filter arose out of Campbell's analysis of loaded lines."

So it was that after years of thought one good thing led to another.

Campbell (right) and John R. Carson both received many awards in recognition of their important contributions to science and telephony. Campbell's work on inductive loading and electrical filters and Carson's invention of single-sideband transmission increased the range and efficiency of telecommunications channels.

all the way to Denver. And by 1913 a loaded underground cable connected Boston and Washington. Also, after nearly 20 years of effort, the first means for getting more than one voice path on a pair of wires had been introduced in 1900. This was the "phantom" circuit, which made it possible to get three telephone circuits from two pairs. The original idea for this had been advanced in 1882, but to reduce the idea to practice it was necessary to develop efficient balanced transformers and a system for transposing the wires at intervals along the line to hold down crosstalk among the circuits—very considerable achievements in those days.

The problems of switching, or interconnection, were no less perplexing than those of transmission. The first commercial switchboard, introduced in New Haven, Connecticut, in 1878, served 21 telephones on eight lines. This had four metal switches, moved by hand, to make connections, and enough switching points to handle the 28 different combinations possible for eight lines. But as the number of customers and lines increased, it was immediately obvious that this way of doing things would not work. With 100 lines, for example, enough switches for 4950 possible combinations would have been necessary. The practical answer was to use flexible interconnecting cords that could be plugged into sockets (called jacks) where the lines terminated in the switchroom. This in turn was fine as long as one operator could handle all the calls. But very soon, as the number of lines continued to increase, it became necessary to terminate every line in multiple fashion in front of several operators, so that when a call came in any operator not busy with other calls could make the connection. It was also necessary, of course, to provide an arrangement whereby each operator, when she answered an incoming request for a connection, could make sure that the line being called was not already busy.

While transmission and switching are conveniently

thought of as separate aspects of the communication system, the early history of telephony shows how interdependent they really are. Thus, when long-distance calls began to be handled, the circuits provided to handle them had to be very different in quality from the local exchange lines. Consequently, setting up a long-distance call required elaborate switchboard procedures, the cooperation of several operators and, more often than not, many long minutes.

A NEW DAY DAWNS

Then came what was to be, next to the telephone itself, the greatest discovery of telephony's first half-century: the vacuum tube. Its impact on both transmission and, ultimately, ease of connection over long distances was profound. The story has been told many times but must find a place here, however briefly.

Even with wire thick as rods, with loading coils and with a form of "repeater" that used carbon contacts to amplify voice currents on long lines, telephone engineers had found it impossible to send the voice farther west than Denver. Something new had to be added—and soon was.

In 1906 Lee de Forest, a brilliant independent inventor, had devised a three-electrode tube that he called the audion. After several years of work and experiment in radiotelegraphy, de Forest brought his audion to the Bell System in 1912. Less than three years later transcontinental telephone service was a fact and in a historic experiment words spoken in Arlington, Virginia, had been heard in Paris.

The audion in its original form was not useful for telephone purposes. However, research by Dr. H. D. Arnold of Western Electric's Engineering Department and Dr. Irving Langmuir of the General Electric Company indicated that a high vacuum inside the tube would probably make it an excellent amplifier

of weak speech currents. And they were right.
By 1914 Western Electric's tube shop was producing satisfactory high-vacuum tubes for installation in long-distance telephone repeaters, and early in 1915 service began between New York and San Francisco. The conquest of distance, if not yet complete (overseas service by radiotelephone was not to start until 1927), was, let us say, "in the works;" the electronic age had begun.

SHEER INVENTIVENESS

The early evolution of switching did not have the benefit of any such striking discoveries as those that produced the electron tube. And as the steps already mentioned suggest, progress in switching techniques appears to have flowed more from sheer inventiveness and ingenuity than from studies like those of George Campbell which so greatly benefited the transmission art.* The first practicable automatic system, invented by Almon B. Strowger in 1889, was installed in La Porte, Indiana, by an independent telephone company in 1892. In this system, forerunner of many others essentially like it, the switches were operated directly, and step by step, by pulses generated at the customer's telephone. In this kind of system, as long as the connection is held, all the equipment used to make it must also be used to maintain it. In contrast, later systems that work on the principle of *common control* use certain parts only briefly to establish the connection and then release them to serve other customers. Such systems are far more efficient and flexible than step-by-step systems and can handle many switching jobs that the latter are not suited for.

*Charles E. Scribner, who was hired by Western Electric in 1877 as a young man of 19 and eventually became the company's chief engineer, took out many patents on switchboard improvements on his way to becoming the most prolific inventor in Bell System history, with a grand total of 497 U.S. and foreign patents in his name.

The earliest common-control systems were developed by Western Electric in a program that began in 1906. These began to go into service within the next 10 to 15 years, and by the time Bell Laboratories was organized, at the end of 1924, a considerable number were in use. How they evolved into present-day systems would get us beyond the scope of this chapter, but a few points may be emphasized.

HOW MUCH IS ENOUGH?

First, interconnection problems included the fundamental question of how much switching apparatus there ought to be. How many people would be calling other people at any one time? If more than enough facilities were provided, the cost would be unnecessarily high; if not enough, the service would be uncertain at best. The problem demanded basic probability studies and in fact generated development of a whole body of applied mathematics known as "trunking theory." Bell System people early in this century made major contributions in the field and laid much of the groundwork for continuing effort to assure that the right facilities would be at the right place at the right time.

A second challenge broad and deep, in both switching and transmission, was to find and develop the most suitable materials for a host of applications. Even long years ago, the telephone system was composed of billions of parts, and for the system to work well at reasonable cost the parts had to be efficient and reliable. Switches and relays had to stand up under incessant use. Materials had to be found that would do more work for less money. The vacuum tubes on which long-distance service then depended had to function without fail at hundreds of locations across the land.

Such considerations impelled AT&T and Western Electric people toward in-depth study of elements, compounds, organic materials, fabrication processes

continued on page 23

Harold D. Arnold

Bell Laboratories' First Director of Research

The name of Harold D. Arnold is most closely associated with development of the high-vacuum electron tube that made transcontinental telephony possible and opened a new era in electrical communications. It is evident, however, from the writings of his contemporaries after his early death in 1933, and from some of his own writings, that his attributes as a thinker and leader could hardly be summed up in terms of that single great success.

Arnold was engaged by Western Electric in 1911 specifically to undertake the development of electron-discharge repeaters. Professor Robert A. Millikan of the University of Chicago had recommended him "as one of the ablest men whose research work I have ever directed and had in classes."

By 1912 Arnold had produced a repeater element employing a mercury arc. This was used to a limited extent but was not very satisfactory. In the same year, however, his attention was called to Dr. Lee de Forest's three-electrode "audion." Arnold recognized its possibilities at once and went to work. Within three years, high-vacuum tubes were in service in the first transcontinental line.

Arnold's contributions to this achievement have been summarized as follows:

He understood that the audion might be transformed into a good amplifier if a high vacuum could be obtained. He developed methods for doing this and for using the space-charge effect of electrons successfully in a practical commercial device. He also developed the principles necessary to assure physical constants in tubes that had to be made in quantity and used interchangeably.

"These advances in electronics," said one review of Arnold's work, "were so quickly accomplished primarily because of his unique ability in research. Instead of looking at the audion as did radio engineers, to whom it had been for years a familiar device, he considered it as a specific instance of the general problem of conduction of electricity through vacua . . . Invariably in attacking a problem he saw it so broadly and philosophically that it usually fell into its proper scientific relationship and disclosed thereby the desired line of attack."

While development of the vacuum-tube amplifier was an exercise in applied (rather than fundamental) research, Arnold had been deeply trained in atomic physics and quite evidently brought to the problem much of the kind of thinking that animates fundamental studies. "Research," he observed years later, "is the effort of the mind to comprehend relationships which no one has previously known." And while he went on to say that in "its finest exemplifications" research is practical as well as theoretical, he seems always to have taken a broad view.

Under his influence research at Bell Laboratories broadened and deepened. He offered a prospectus for wide-ranging action. "Our research problems," he said, "are scattered along the whole frontier of the sciences which contribute to our interests, and extend through the fields of physical and organic chemistry, of metallurgy, of magnetism, of electrical conduction, of radiation, of electronics, of acoustics, of phonetics, of optics, of mathematics, of mechanics, and even of physiology, of psychology and of meteorology."

Quite a laundry list. Arnold also understood that freedom for the researcher was essential to accomplishment. Invention, he said, was a valuable part of a research department's output. However, "invention is not to be scheduled or coerced; it follows research through the operation of genius; and the best that any department can do to promote it is to provide a suitable environment."

Clearly, the man who came to work in 1911 to develop an improved repeater advanced the art of communications not only directly, through his success with the vacuum tube, but through his influence on the development of Bell Laboratories itself.

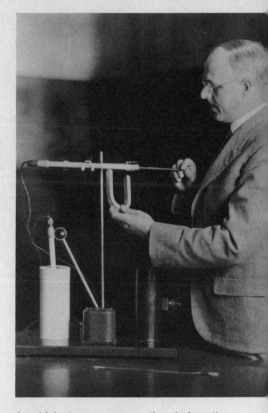

Arnold lectures on magnetism before the American Association for the Advancement of Science in 1931.

22

Congestion of telephone lines in cities was unsightly, and the wires were exposed to weather and accidental damage. In 1899, Bell engineers devised "inductive loading," which greatly increased the distance that wires could transmit voice signals. Inductive loading improved transmission quality enough that lines could be run in cables underground. This photo shows Broadway and John Street, New York City, in 1890 (inset) and around 1910 after the introduction of underground cable.

and quality assurance techniques. As one example of results, the tube most commonly used in telephone repeaters in 1917 had a life of about six weeks. A tube introduced 18 years later (after a succession of intermediate improvements) used only one-tenth as much power to heat the filament and could be expected to operate continuously for several years.

A third vitally important field of work in the pre-Bell Laboratories years was the early development of "carrier" systems, which use different frequency bands, separated by electrical wave filters, to carry a number of conversations simultaneously over the same transmission path. This is described briefly in Chapter 3, "The Transmission Story." The point to note here is that successful application of the carrier principle to telephony rested on two main foundations. One was development of the vacuum tube, which could generate high-frequency carrier waves as well as amplify voice currents; the other, the fundamental studies of George Campbell, which led him to invent the electrical wave filter in 1915.

A great deal of other work in the first quarter of this century was essential to the furnishing of acceptable service at reasonable cost. Telephone instruments themselves were improved, although they still had a long way to go. Research produced

A circuit development laboratory in Bell Laboratories'
West Street building in New York City during the 1920's.
Engineers had to fit benches and equipment into existing
architecture as best they could. By contrast, today's
laboratories have flexible, modular design, moveable
walls and other features that make them more efficient
and comfortable.

24

magnetic alloys far and away more efficient than any ever known before. And the vacuum tube, it turned out, not only solved the basic problem of distance but also revealed the need to solve others—for the power to amplify carried with it the power to show up defects. The new electronic techniques also made it possible to define standards and measure performance more closely than ever before.

The whole system became more sensitive and at the same time more susceptible to improvement. Developments in "network theory" led to transmission regulators that automatically compensated for changes in temperature and other factors that distorted voice currents. Devices were fashioned to suppress electrical echoes on long circuits. Still other equipment compressed the range of speech sounds at the transmitting end and expanded it again at the receiving end; this helped to reduce the effect of noise on the line. And overall, the need for dependability of components in increasingly complex systems prompted development of statistical procedures for quality control that rank among the landmark inventions of modern times.

THE KEY TO SUCCESS

These instances are perhaps enough to demonstrate the point of greatest importance—that the key to success in telephony was an organized program to expand and refine the technology on a foundation of accurate knowledge. This lesson had to be learned, to be sure, but it was learned in time to make the Bell System one of the few enterprises in the United States that early in the 20th century departed from custom to undertake their own fundamental research.

The sequence of events, in the organizational sense, was briefly as follows:

In the 1880's the American Bell Telephone Company (predecessor of AT&T) maintained in Boston what was called a Mechanical Department. The people in the department studied problems and worked to test and improve apparatus, protect equipment against strong electrical currents, and the like. In 1891 an Engineers Department was formed to work on construction and operating methods. In 1902 the two departments were merged, with something under 200 employees.

That was one technical organization. Another was the Engineering Department of Western Electric, the manufacturing company that became a part of the Bell System in 1882. Most of its members were in New York; others were in Chicago. Their job was to develop and design equipment for manufacture.

In 1907 John J. Carty, who at that time became AT&T's chief engineer, moved to pull things together. The Boston people came to New York. So likewise did many of Western Electric's Chicago engineers. Soon afterward, in 1911, Carty reported formation of a fundamental research group as a branch of Western's Engineering Department. This, he said, was set up to include "in its personnel the best talent available, and in its equipment the best facilities possible for the highest grade research laboratory work."

Only three years later President Theodore N. Vail of AT&T reported to his stockholders that some 550 "carefully selected" engineers and scientists were working at Bell System headquarters. "Among them," Vail wrote with evident pride, "are former professors and instructors of our universities, postgraduate students and other graduates holding various engineering and scientific degrees from 70 different scientific schools and universities, 60 American and 10 foreign institutions of learning being represented.

"No other telephone company," he affirmed, "no government telephone administration in the world, has a staff and scientific equipment such as this."

A MAN WITH BIG IDEAS

It should not be inferred that all fundamental studies in the Bell System began suddenly in 1911.

Indeed, as noted earlier, the mathematician George Campbell was at work as early as 1897 and there were a few other students of basic problems in the early years. Unquestionably, however, the impetus toward a more intensive attack on the great problems of telephony came with Theodore N. Vail's election to the presidency of AT&T in 1907.

Vail had been general manager of the American Bell Telephone Company in the 1880's. He was a man then—and always—with big ideas. It was at his behest, for example, that the articles of incorporation of AT&T, which was later to succeed American Bell as the central company of the Bell System, stated the company's intent to provide telephone connections between cities all over the country and "by cable and other appropriate means, with the rest of the known world." This at a time when the "electricians" had only just succeeded in providing service between Boston and New York!

Part of Vail's purpose in insisting on this kind of language, as his correspondence shows, was his wish that the scope of AT&T's corporate charter would keep the company free from hampering legal restrictions, for previously state corporation laws

In 1896, the Western Electric Company bought property on West Street in New York City. Piles were driven into the sandy soil as support for the building that was to house the Engineering Department. In 1925, this Department, with a portion of the Patent Department, formed a new organization incorporated as "Bell Telephone Laboratories." In 1934, AT&T's Department of Development and Research was transferred to Bell Laboratories.

had placed severe constraints on the raising of capital. Nevertheless, this was a staggering concept in 1885. "The rest of the known world," indeed. The words brilliantly reaffirmed Mr. Bell's original vision of "this grand system" and gave dramatic expression to Vail's own dream and goal of *universal service.*

And there is the heart of the matter. In the last analysis, it was the tantalizing, difficult, distant, but still-perhaps-attainable goal that energized Bell System research and development and gave them their vitality. It has been said that until the time of the telephone, with all its promise and its baffling mysteries, no business organization had ever been so deeply challenged. This may well be correct, but

the significant point is that something more than a mere multitude of difficulties made the challenge exciting and prompted energetic response. It was not the problems, but the goal, that inspired the moving of mountains.

Vail had departed from the Bell System in 1887, only two years after giving AT&T the kind of charge expressed in its charter. He left because he did not think the American Bell directors were letting him do all that he felt could be done. Called back as AT&T president twenty years later, he gave the business a second charge that swiftly renewed its vitality. The impact on research and development was tremendous, as results so soon made clear.

AN EVOLUTIONARY STEP

One reason for the consolidation engineered by Carty in 1907, it is true, was to help control costs; this was a year of economic strain and what the history books still call financial panic. However, the move had other aspects of much greater permanent importance. As President H. B. Thayer of AT&T wrote later, in the year when Bell Laboratories was formed, "it brought to one point scientific study and research, manufacturing experience and operating experience and brought them all to bear most effectively on each problem." Today we might gently amend Mr. Thayer's comment to say that such was certainly the intent of the 1907 change; that ensuing results attested its good sense; and that formation of Bell Laboratories 18 years later as an entity having its own character and power to attract talent—but in closest touch also with the needs of both the builders and users of the systems it develops—seemed a natural further evolutionary step.

Two small Bell Laboratories field stations in New Jersey later became major locations. Shown above is the "Turkey Farm," a building erected in 1930 at Holmdel for investigation of shortwave radio communication. Here, far from city-made electrical noise, engineers studied problems of radio transmission and reception. Research at Holmdel in the 1930's helped establish reliable long-distance radiotelephony and as a byproduct founded the science of radio astronomy. At left is the Whippany laboratory as it appeared in 1935. Established in 1926, Whippany grew to become a multi-building complex. During and after World War II, it was the center of Bell Laboratories work on government contracts. Now, work on power equipment and mobile radiotelephone systems is conducted there for the Bell System.

Speaking from New York in 1892, Alexander Graham Bell opens the first telephone line to Chicago—a link 900 miles long. Greater distances were then impracticable; voices faded and became indistinct. In 1911, Bell System engineers were able to extend the line to Denver, a total distance of 2100 miles, using very thick copper wires and loading coils. The next step in the conquest of distance had to await the vacuum tube.

THE TRANSMISSION STORY

As we have seen, it took nearly 40 years to bridge the continent by telephone. From 1915 on, however, the pace quickened. An immediate reason was the marvelous high-vacuum electron tube, which could not only amplify voice currents but also generate and modulate electromagnetic waves. More basic, however, was the deliberate organization of research by Vail and Carty that had led to the exploitation of the electron tube in the first place. Gathering momentum, this effort produced a stream of advances that have continued to the present time and which today, in fact, suggest the likelihood of future change as striking as any in the past.

Transmission systems have developed, not from invention alone, but by reason of a wide range of interactive work in mathematical theory, physics, chemistry, acoustics, and materials science; and by reason also of precise measurement techniques and innovations in processes of fabrication and manufacture. All of these have come together, as new knowledge has been acquired, in systems that can carry increasing amounts of information with great fidelity and at decreasing unit costs.

COMMUNICATIONS IN THE NEWS

In the 25 years prior to World War II, freshets of novelty in communications repeatedly made news. In 1915, the year transcontinental telephone service started, historic experiments by AT&T engineers also succeeded in sending voices from Virginia across the oceans to Paris and Honolulu and thereby established the possibility of overseas radiotelephony. A few years later, listeners in San Francisco heard, through loudspeakers, the words and music of a memorial service at the tomb of the unknown soldier in Arlington, Virginia. Not long afterward, in 1924, telephone wires carried the first coast-to-coast radio broadcast. Also in the 1920's, a submarine cable provided a single voice channel between Key West and Havana; news associations started to send pictures over telephone lines specially arranged by Bell engineers; and a new ocean cable developed by Western Electric's research department at government request handled telegraph messages four times as fast as the older telegraph cables under the Atlantic.

In 1927 radiotelephone service began between New York and London. In the dozen years that followed, systems that bounced waves off the ionosphere, 200,000 feet above the earth, extended voice communications to country after country around the world.* At the end of the decade of the 1920's one could even telephone to and from the liner *Leviathan* at sea. This prompted comedian Fred Allen, on the Broadway stage, to amuse audiences by pretending to reach an otherwise unreachable nearby New York City number by the stratagem of having his call routed out to the ship and back.

Service to coastal and harbor vessels followed soon after. Also in the 1930's, Bell Laboratories developed aircraft radio equipment that set standards widely adopted. The first experimental long-distance television transmission in the United States was demonstrated by the Laboratories in 1927, and this was followed a few years later by experimental transmission of scenes in color. Teletypewriter exchange service, whereby typed messages could be sent to and from machines interconnected through switching centers in the same way that telephones are interconnected, was introduced in 1931.

CARRIER TELEPHONY

Less newsworthy, perhaps, at the time, but of profound consequence, was the development of "carrier" systems to multiply the number of conversations that might be carried over the same conductors.† It is difficult to overstate the importance of this. The conquest of distance had been, of course, the first essential, but for general public use "long distance" has certain obvious limits; worldwide service is—well, worldwide, with some help nowadays from satellites in space. Carrier systems, however, are not bounded in the same way. From four circuits to a dozen to hundreds to thousands and then to tens and hundreds of thousands . . . and from voice communications to the transmission of information in every form . . . that has been the story and the end is not yet. Today we take this abundance for granted. Its principal source, both past and present, has been the work of scientists and engineers at AT&T, Western Electric and Bell Laboratories.

The first carrier telephone system in commercial service, providing four additional circuits over one pair of wires, ran between Baltimore and Pittsburgh. This was in 1918. By 1938, over numerous open-wire lines, wire pairs were able to carry as many as 16 telephone circuits and by 1937 similar techniques were being applied to pairs of wire in long-distance cables. In 1942 an underground-cable carrier system reached from coast to coast. Before that time, however, the first cables using coaxial conductors— each of which consists of a wire carefully centered within a small-diameter tube—were in regular use over two short routes. A system using two such conductors could handle—eureka!—600 simultaneous

---

*Somewhat precariously, however, for atmospheric conditions and magnetic storms sometimes made conversation difficult. In 1935, as a demonstration, President W. S. Gifford of AT&T and Vice President T. G. Miller, sitting in adjoining rooms in New York, talked with each other over a combined wire and radio circuit that traveled 23,000 miles around the world. The program called for two conversations, the first planned as a trial or rehearsal and the second to be "official." However, when the trial succeeded gloriously Mr. Gifford, a practical man, decided that this was sufficient and that the official call—which just possibly might not succeed as well—could be dispensed with.

---

†Carrier systems are so called because the currents or signals that contain information are carried on high-frequency radio waves guided along the physical conductors (or, in the case of microwave radio systems, beamed from transmitting to receiving antennas). Generally, the wider the bands of frequencies that can be used as carriers, the more the information that can be handled. Increases in bandwidth are achieved through ability to create and control increasingly high frequencies, with correspondingly shorter waves. For a reason obvious from the foregoing, carrier systems are often referred to as *broadband* systems.

In 1915, the introduction of vacuum-tube amplifiers to boost signal strength on telephone lines made it possible to extend telephone service across the continent. Above is the scene at the Pacific Telephone and Telegraph Company, San Francisco, when the first transcontinental telephone line was opened. The connection required stringing four copper wires across 13 states, on 130,000 telephone poles. Seated at the table, third from left, is Thomas A. Watson, Alexander Graham Bell's assistant in experiments that led to the invention of the telephone.

conversations or, alternatively, a television circuit in each direction.

Later developments, as we shall see, make this figure look small. But even in these earlier years the multiplication of transmission pathways, which would have been economically impossible if limited to a process of adding more and more wires, had tremendous impact. In 1926, when Bell Laboratories was a year old, only two per cent of the Bell System's three million miles of long-distance circuits were in carrier systems. Twenty-five years later nearly two-thirds of 30 million miles of circuits were so provided.* The increase reflects, fundamentally, public acceptance and usage as innovative technology made improved service available at more favorable costs and reduced rates.

PIONEERS OF TRANSMISSION

As noted on page 18, it was invention of the electric wave filter by George Campbell in 1915 (the patent was issued two years later) that opened the way to carrier telephony.† In the next two decades Campbell, Harry Nyquist, Hendrik Bode and others at Bell Laboratories developed and refined the basic theory that governs design of the electrical networks used to filter and shape signals in nearly all electronic systems.

*Today practically all long-distance transmission in the United States is over carrier systems.

†The filter passes signals in a certain frequency band and blocks signals in all other bands. In a carrier telephone system, each voice signal is carried at a different frequency and each frequency has its own filter. This is why many conversations can be carried simultaneously over the same conductors.

In 1915 also, John R. Carson of AT&T, analyzing the nature of radio transmission, showed that either side of a modulated carrier wave could carry as much information as the two sides together. Thus was born *single-sideband* transmission, a technique of fundamental importance in making efficient use of frequency space (see page 34). This was applied to the first wire carrier systems and to overseas radiotelephone circuits. It has subsequently been used on both coaxial cable and microwave radio systems, thanks to related inventions and developments that include remarkably selective crystal filters, crystal oscillators that govern precise frequencies, high-power transmitting amplifiers, and receivers

This Ford tri-motor, known as the "tin goose," was fitted out as a radio laboratory and operated during Bell Laboratories' early years to study ground-to-plane radio communications, radio altimeters and direction-finding equipment. These studies, begun in 1928, continued for ten years.

automatically tuned and controlled. As a single example of these supporting inventions, it was in 1937 that W. P. Mason, one of Bell Laboratories' most fertile inventors, devised a method for cutting crystals so that they would remain virtually unaffected by temperature changes. This was an achievement of great consequence in controlling carrier system frequencies.

A third basic development in transmission was the negative feedback amplifier invented by Harold S. Black in 1927. Black showed that, by feeding part of an amplifier's output back to the input, the amplifier could be made practically distortion-free (see page 39). This principle has been essential to the success of long-distance multichannel systems, which require large numbers of repeaters (distortionless amplifiers) in tandem to keep the fragile information-carrying currents from fading away. Here again mathematical theory, developed mainly by Nyquist and Bode, provided the basis for efficient use of the invention. It is interesting to note also that the negative-feedback principle has been applied to the development of a wide range of electrical, mechanical and chemical systems and that Nyquist's work has provided a basic guide to their design.

Still another Bell Laboratories contribution during this period was the development of noise theory, which establishes the limits of performance in communications devices. With later mathematical refinements, noise theory also makes it possible to deal precisely with random current fluctuations in electrical devices and networks. Other research, led by Harvey Fletcher, on the nature of speech and hearing, included precise measurement (for the first time) of the sensitivity of the ear and the human ability to perceive complex sounds under varying conditions. This knowledge established guidelines of great value in aiding the design of telephones and transmission systems with improved "hearability."

continued on page 35

John R. Carson

Inventor of Single-Sideband Transmission

The heading above states the accomplishment for which John R. Carson is most famous. His thought and achievement, however, were deeper and wider than any single instance would suggest.

"His forte," wrote Lloyd Espenschied in a 1956 article for the *Dictionary of American Biography,* years after Carson's death in 1940, "was the application of mathematics to electromagnetic wave propagation over wires and through space, and the development of network theory. Some 50 scientific papers, marked by masterly exposition, together with 25 U. S. patents, attest his profundity and creativeness. In developing network theory he canvassed the field of mathematical methods of analysis, and found in Oliver Heaviside's operational calculus a powerful instrument that had not been generally recognized or developed. What was perhaps his greatest scientific contribution was the placing of this procedure on a logical and rigorous basis available to the network engineer . . ." A few of the many subjects he studied mathematically were the effects of the earth, and the ocean, on long conductors; the nature of frequency modulation; the problem of static; and, as mentioned on page 64, waveguide transmission.

Carson joined AT&T, in a department that later became part of Bell Laboratories, just at the time when preparations were being made for the first experimental radiotelephone transmission across the oceans. His first challenge was to analyze mathematically the role of the vacuum tube in modulating a carrier wave, i.e., impressing on it the voice-frequency signal.

One of his associates, B. W. Kendall, was finding that reception of the modulated wave could be improved by introducing in the receiver additional energy identical in frequency with that of the carrier. Quickly Carson saw that if this could be done, the carrier need not be transmitted in the first place but could be resupplied at the receiving end.

However, that was not all. When a carrier wave is modulated, the resulting signal includes, along with the carrier, two side frequencies for each frequency component in the original voice (or other) signal. One of these sidebands is above the carrier frequency and the other an equal distance below it. Since either one contains all the intelligence in the signal, Carson proposed that only one of the two be transmitted.

Thus were both power and channel space saved. Single-sideband transmission came into general use in both wire and radio transmission and has long been so familiar to communications engineers that it is difficult to appreciate what an innovation it was. To filter out one of the two sidebands, by the way, required Campbell's earlier underlying invention of the wave filter—another interesting instance of how inventions fit together in communication systems.

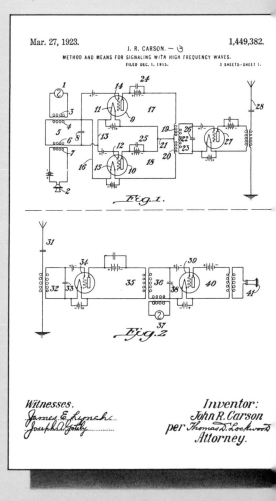

These are drawings from the U.S. patent granted to Carson showing the electrical circuit that made single sideband transmission possible. The technique helped increase the efficiency and call-carrying capacity of communication systems.

PROGRESS IN BOTH CABLE AND RADIO TECHNOLOGIES

The use of coaxial cable for broadband telephone transmission was the result of a unique system invented by Lloyd Espenschied and H. A. Affel of Bell Laboratories in 1929; successive developments have enormously increased the capacity of coaxial systems. Reference has also been made above to telephoto service and experimental TV transmission. In both fields, studies by Nyquist aided understanding of the basic problems, and research by Herbert Ives and Frank Gray laid much of the groundwork for the demonstrations conducted in the 1920's and for the introduction of TV network service after World War II.

In the first half of the century (and the first half also of Bell Laboratories' first 50 years) telephone transmission was predominantly over wire and cable systems. The excitement of radio was limited mainly to broadcasting and overseas telephony. However, basic concepts and theories of the kind touched on above applied to radio as well as to wire transmission. So too did intensive, persistent effort to understand electron tubes and improve their performance. H. D. Arnold's success in making de Forest's audion a useful amplifier has already been noted. Other successes followed—for example, a practical cathode design that nearly all tube manufacturers adopted; transmitting tubes that made high-power broadcasting practical and overseas radiotelephony possible; analyses and measurements that for years provided the basis for tube design and circuitry; and, not least of all, the circuits themselves that could use electron tubes effectively to generate, modulate and amplify signals.

Not until electronic gear could be devised that would generate and control *microwaves* (radio waves at frequencies in billions of cycles per second) could

Research at Bell Laboratories has added greatly to understanding of plastics used for wire insulation. Chemists have tracked down the causes — and cures — for cracking in plastic insulation on telephone wires. Here, plastic-insulated wires are subjected to varying temperatures in ovens that simulate natural conditions.

radio be used in the nationwide telephone network, for lower frequencies refused to travel from point to point in narrow beams. The skills to achieve microwave radio systems, however, were steadily building—and along the way Bell Laboratories

Mounting Bell Laboratories' 170-pound Telstar I satellite to
a Thor-Delta rocket for its journey into orbit in 1962.
Telstar I demonstrated the feasibility of relaying telephone
calls, television and data across oceans and continents
by an orbiting satellite. A great many Bell Laboratories
achievements, including the transistor and the solar battery,
made satellite communications possible.

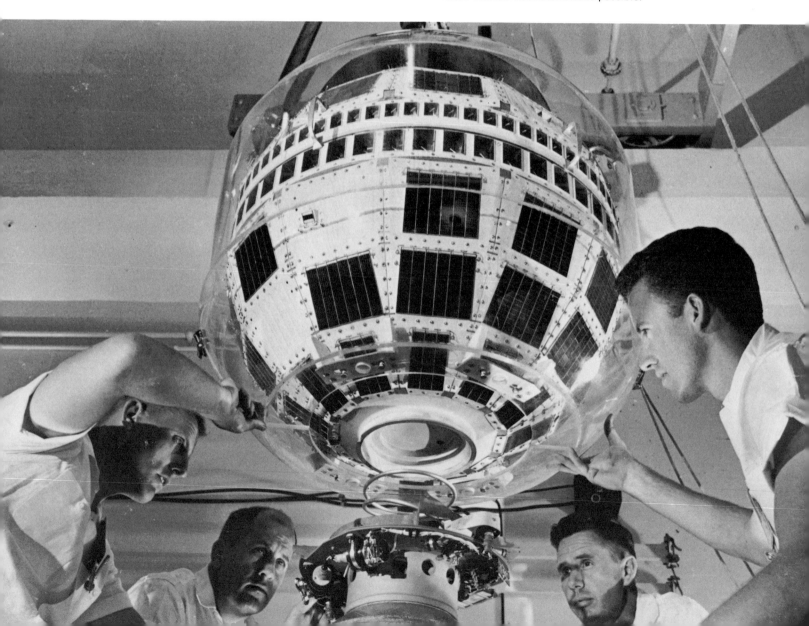

research workers investigated every aspect of radio transmission and reception. They made exhaustive studies of wave propagation. They observed natural phenomena and measured their effects.* They designed antennas and other gear and analyzed their performance. They collaborated with other organizations to gather the detailed information needed to plan and design worldwide shortwave radiotelephone systems. And they created the rhombic antenna, which was basic to the rapid development of global service in the 1930's.

TRANSMISSION DYNAMICS

Microwave radio systems exemplify so well how continuous effort pays off that they are treated separately beginning on page 57. Similar stories could be told about other systems, but we shall have to deal with those more rapidly. Five overall points may be kept in mind.

First, since World War II transmission pathways have increased in fantastic numbers to handle continuously increasing demand.

Second, invention of the transistor at Bell Laboratories soon after the war, and the ensuing development of semiconductor technology, have already had strong impact and will have much more.

Third, the use of electronics in transmission, once economical over long distances only, is becoming increasingly practical over short distances too.

Fourth, as usable bands of frequencies have been made wider, and hence capable of handling television and other complex signals as well as voice, parallel effort has already had some success in reducing the bandwidth needed for good transmission. For example, means have been devised to lower the bandwidth required for Picturephone service.

Fifth, guided by information theory, fundamental change in the very nature of transmission is under way; i.e., from analog (wave) to digital (pulse).

The separate story (Chapter 4) on microwave systems should not be taken to mean that progress in other directions has been less striking. Coaxial cable systems, in fact, have increased in capacity even more markedly. By the end of 1949 some 7600 miles of the first type of coaxial system, able to handle 600 simultaneous conversations over each pair of coaxial conductors, were already in service. Four years later Bell Laboratories came up with a new system that increased the figure to 1860, and in 1967, the next system increased it again to 3600. (Note here the impact of transistor technology.) The latest system, placed in operation in 1974 between Pittsburgh and St. Louis, can handle 108,000 conversations over ten pairs of coaxials contained in the same cable, with another pair provided for automatic protection in case a working pair should fail.

While both coaxial and microwave systems were growing, new carrier systems were also being developed for conventional cable and wire lines on short routes. In 1956 came the first transatlantic telephone cable, soon to be followed by a succession of other cables (likewise increasing in capacity) in Atlantic, Pacific and Caribbean waters.† Late in the 1950's "over-the-horizon" systems connected Florida with Cuba and the Bahamas by scattering microwaves up to the troposphere and down again.

---

*It was in the course of doing this that Karl Jansky made the observations that led to the new science of radio astronomy. See page 107.

†The high quality of ocean cable service had an immediate impact. In the year after the first cable went to work, transatlantic calls doubled. With the subsequent growth of cable and satellite systems, the total volume of overseas calls in 1973 was 35 times what it had been two decades earlier.

On the ocean floor off Rhode Island, the sea plow designed by Bell Laboratories is towed by a cable-laying ship. In this operation, the sea plow is digging a trench two feet deep and burying a Bell System transatlantic cable. Off-shore sections of many cables are buried to protect them against accidental damage from fishing trawlers.

In the same years Dataphone® services became available for the first time over the nationwide switched network as well as over private lines. In 1960, while an ingenious system called TASI (Time Assignment Speech Interpolation) was doubling the capacity of the first ocean cables by switching voices automatically among different channels as talkers paused in their speech, Bell Laboratories engineers were also bouncing microwave signals off the moon. Later in the year, they transmitted speech from coast to coast by reflecting signals from a big plastic balloon named *Echo* that had been hoisted into orbit by NASA. Two years later, in July of 1962, the world's first actively powered communications satellite, Telstar™, conceived and designed at the Laboratories, relayed both speech and television across the Atlantic to demonstrate the feasibility of satellite communications.

DIGITAL TRANSMISSION

Meanwhile, back at the ranch—which is to say, in this instance, under city streets—an entirely new system was handling conversations between certain metropolitan-area exchanges in streams of coded pulses. This first-of-its-kind *digital* wire transmission system carries up to 24 conversations on two pairs of wire—one for each direction of transmission—in cables already in place, and uses relatively simple equipment every mile or so to regenerate the pulses before they fade away. The apparatus at the terminals, too, is less costly than that required for *analog* systems which (in contrast to the digital) transmit electrical currents analogous to the sound waves created by speech. Today this digital mode is being applied to millions of pairs of wire in big-city cables; to other cables up to 500 miles in length; to the first long-distance circular waveguide (a finely made, specially constructed hollow tube) which is being evaluated over a short route in New Jersey and can handle, when fully equipped, about 230,000

continued on page 41

Harold S. Black

The Daring Young Man on the Ferryboat

Legend, at least, has it that one day in 1927 a young man of 29, on his way by ferry across the Hudson to his laboratory at 463 West Street, New York City, was seized by a daring idea for a new kind of amplifier circuit. (He had been working for years, be it noted, on the problem that he hoped this new idea might solve.) Hastily he sketched it on his newspaper, along with a few lines of mathematics. When he arrived at the laboratory, paper in one hand and his pipe in the other, Harold Black proposed to the first people he came upon the negative feedback circuit, an invention now generally regarded as one of the great landmarks of discovery in the communications art.

Negative feedback is a technique for correcting error and distortion in the process of amplifying communication signals. Part of the signal coming out of the amplifier is sent back through a "loop" and compared with what went in; distortions introduced by the amplifier can then be identified and corrected.

It sounds tremendous, and it is—but for years a really satisfactory negative feedback circuit proved very hard to achieve. Many of Black's associates at Bell Laboratories discounted the possibilities. "The invention of negative feedback," one of his laboratory assistants later recalled, "had all the initial impact of a blow with a wet noodle."*

Several factors combined to alter the case. One was Black's own certainty that the thing could be done. To quote his former assistant again, "Harold did not even approach the question of stability—he simply assumed that it (the circuit) did not 'sing' . . .

---

*A. C. Dickieson, later a Bell Laboratories vice president.

and the advantages he pointed to were so compelling as to drive us through years of failure."

Second, mathematical physicists came to the rescue with a body of theory that described the process in accurate detail and so guided the developers' efforts. Third, new devices, components and measuring equipment gave them better tools to work with. Finally, sheer necessity drove them on, for it soon enough became apparent that the economics of long-distance telephone service demanded new techniques that could not be used successfully unless they embodied Black's invention.

"It was this pressing need," his former assistant concludes, "plus Black's stubbornness, that carried us through years of adversity."

As the years passed, feedback theory also generated development of automatic control systems and the basic principle came to be regarded as one of the cornerstones of modern engineering.

Today a "new" method of amplifying analog signals, first demonstrated in the laboratory in 1972, is getting serious attention. It is called feed*forward* error correction and it was originally conceived (you guessed it) by Harold Black, even before he invented feed*back*.

Why this turn of events? For one thing, there appears to be an upper limit to the transmission speeds that feedback amplifiers can handle. Systems that might produce many more voice paths than are obtained today on the highest-capacity coaxial cable would operate too fast for the feedback loop. Feedforward, however, produces two parallel waves, one for the main signal and one for accumulated errors; these travel together so that errors can be corrected in effect within the same time frame.

More complex than feedback, feedforward presents problems that long seemed overly formidable. Now, however, the problems have been attacked with telling results. Watching these results, by invitation, when they were first demonstrated in 1972, was the man who started it all. His reaction was quick. "Hooray!" Harold Black shouted.

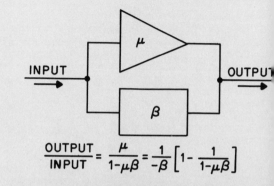

$$\frac{\text{OUTPUT}}{\text{INPUT}} = \frac{\mu}{1-\mu\beta} = \frac{1}{-\beta}\left[1 - \frac{1}{1-\mu\beta}\right]$$

At the top are a diagram and mathematical equation describing Black's concept of negative feedback — an idea that had a revolutionary impact on the design of electronic circuits. The photo shows Black with some of the amplifying equipment that used his idea for reducing distortion by reversing some of the amplifier output and feeding it back into the input.

conversations at a time; and to a radio system that promises to make excellent use of ultra-high-frequency millimeter waves, which are far more abundant than the waves now employed in radio relay communications.

Already it seems a longer way back to that first carrier system of 1918 than the mere passage of years would suggest. Moreover, it seems likely that near-term developments will leave today behind as quickly as today has outrun the past. For instance, engineers at Bell Laboratories indicate that to double, once again, the capacity of these already astoundingly capacious systems—microwave, coaxial and wave-guide—would be challenging but technically quite possible, if and when such increases were needed. And beyond any such development—or perhaps ahead of it—lies the prospect of transmission through pulses of light.

CIRCUITS OF LIGHT

For years it has been said, *"Some day* exploitation of the light spectrum, which is 1000 times wider than the radio spectrum, may permit broadband transmission of *all* forms of intelligence into every home and office, at an attractive price." And now a first step in light transmission seems close at hand. This is the use of glass fibers of utmost purity to carry broad bands of frequencies under city streets from central office to central office. The basic tools for doing this—the transmitters, modulators, amplifiers and other components needed for an optical communications system—already exist in at least workable form and have been successfully tried out in the laboratory. Moreover, the reason for considering this kind of system is not a bit "far out." It is very practical. The underground network of power, gas, steam, water and communication facilities in some big cities today is astonishingly complex. In many places there is hardly room for more, and major additions are becoming very costly to install. But hair-thin glass fibers, packed in tiny cables that

might carry as many communication signals as thousands of telephone wires, might be fitted into spaces between existing underground structures in such a way as to minimize construction costs. Therefore, while the "ultimate" arrival of optical communications for home and office may still be far off, some transmission over circuits of light may come to pass within a few years.

MORE ABOUT DIGITAL SYSTEMS

Not devices alone, but devices and ideas come together over time, interact, and influence each other

These cables in a test tank remain watertight even with their protective outer sheaths perforated. The secret is a special petroleum jelly, developed by Bell Laboratories in 1969, that fills the air spaces in the cable, preventing water from entering. This and other techniques for protecting calls become increasingly important as the Bell System places more cable underground.

For a new digital transmission system, Bell Laboratories engineers developed a cable that could transmit signals more than twice as far as earlier cables before the signals needed regenerating. Here, in 1971, pairs of wires from the cable are separated for testing.

to guide development of transmission systems. The rise of digital transmission is a good example.

It was back in 1937 that A. H. Reeves of I.T.T. made the first suggestion for handling voice communications by Pulse-Code Modulation (PCM)—the stream-of-coded-pulses method now being extended under city streets, as mentioned above, and also finding its way into long-distance systems. But PCM could not be made practical at that time for two main reasons. One was that it needs much more frequency space—bandwidth—than analog transmission, and until the 1960's this could not be

spared. The other reason was that PCM also requires a precision and speed of operation that could not be achieved at reasonable cost with the devices then available.

Now, however, see what has happened. New solid-state devices combine precision, speed and economy. Guided by information theory, which was set forth by Claude E. Shannon of Bell Laboratories in 1948, engineers can design systems both reliable and economical. Also, the bandwidth PCM demands is available in abundance—great wide reaches of it. So the engineer can afford to trade bandwidth for PCM's advantages.

One advantage is that PCM repeaters simply regenerate enfeebled pulses and there are no accumulating increments of distortion as this process is repeated on a long line. Also, terminal gear costs less and this is of particular advantage on short lines. But there are other values as well. For example, the "mix" of different kinds of signals—voice, data, Picturephone—can be as desired; the proportion of each will not make it more difficult to handle the others. Data can move with less processing than is needed in analog systems. Also, digital systems, interleaving in time (in millionths of a second) the pulses of many different voice or data signals, fit beautifully with new long-distance switching systems that make interconnections in the same way—that is, by slotting pulses at timed intervals to determine their direction (see page 77).

Furthermore, it turns out that some of the transmission media offering greatest opportunities for abundance of circuits actually require the digital mode. The circular waveguide, for instance, is inherently suited for PCM. So too is the new experimental millimeter-wave radio system. Millimeter waves, being about as long as the diameter of small raindrops, are much affected by rainfall.

Digital transmission, using repeaters that need only detect and regenerate pulses before they disappear completely, is the only method suitable for millimeter-wave radio communication.

Still another remarkable aspect of digital transmission was disclosed only a few years ago—namely, that a digital system for handling data communications at high speeds can be added to existing long-distance microwave systems on a segment of the frequency band that is not generally used for carrying voice signals. Taking advantage of this opportunity, Bell Laboratories has developed a Data Under Voice (DUV) system for handling data over a network interconnecting many of our major cities.

COMPETING TECHNOLOGIES

Perhaps the most striking aspect of the half-century transmission story is the one most emphasized in these pages—that is, the seemingly endless multiplication of electrical pathways and the tremendous economies of scale that have been achieved. It is this, fundamentally, that has made modern telecommunications possible. And not the least important contributing factor has been that transmission development at Bell Laboratories has followed not one road, or two, but every road that has shown promise.

In the late 1940's, for example, Charles H. Townes, then at Bell Laboratories, worked on gas spectroscopy. This was the foundation for his work in the early 1950's, at Columbia University, that led to a low-noise amplifier called the maser.* Following up fast, development engineers soon produced a maser

*Maser is the acronym for Microwave Amplification by Stimulated Emission of Radiation, and Laser has the same kind of meaning except that the first letter stands for Light. As may be surmised, the principle is the same for both the microwave spectrum and the light spectrum.

In 1957, three Bell Laboratories scientists, Harold Seidel, George Feher and Derrick Scovil (left to right), demonstrated for the first time that solids could be made to amplify through the "maser" principle. They went on to develop the ruby maser amplifier, which provided the ultrasensitive broadband amplification needed in ground stations for phone calls and television signals transmitted from the orbiting Telstar satellite.

Circuits in the "range extender with gain" are tested in a transmission development laboratory at Bell Laboratories in Whippany, N.J. This equipment, which went into service in April, 1972, boosts signaling and transmission on the long wires that connect rural customers with telephone switching offices. The device permits the use of thinner copper wire, reducing material costs.

built around a crystal of aluminum oxide; i.e., a ruby. As it has turned out, masers have never found wide use, for alternatives have been adequate at less cost. However, the ruby maser, plus the traveling-wave tube, plus the transistor, plus the so-called "horn-reflector" antenna, plus the solar battery that Bell Laboratories people devised as a variant, so to speak, of transistor technology—these together, all of them, made it possible to take a realistic chance on developing the Telstar satellite, the first active communications satellite and the pathfinder across the heavens, one wants to say, for worldwide satellite communications.

Later Townes and Arthur Schawlow—the former then a consultant to Bell Laboratories and the latter a member of its technical staff—proposed the laser, which is to light waves what the maser is to microwaves. Very quickly this too became an important order of business. The result is that Laboratories people probably know as much about lasers as any group in the world and have produced more kinds than any other laboratory, including lasers closest to being practical for use in communications. In the same years, however, as we have seen, microwave, coaxial, satellite and waveguide systems have also grown in both present function and future promise.

Thus developments in different technologies compete with each other and may also, in time, complement each other. And new combinations may present themselves at any moment—as when materials science, for instance, produces a rare crystalline compound that can become a semiconductor diode that winks light millions of times a second and may just possibly be the right engine of luminescence for optical fibers that began to be studied and refined because Townes and Schawlow back in the 1950's proposed the laser. Also, however (and this is equally important), maybe someone else can

continued on page 47

Harry Nyquist

Inventions Furnished on Request

It is said of Harry Nyquist that time and again, when an invention was needed to help solve a problem, a vice president of Bell Laboratories with whose work he was closely associated would turn to him and say, "Harry, why don't you invent this?"—whereupon Nyquist, in a matter of days, weeks, or months, as the case might be, would proceed to do so.

Yet, as was also reported at the time of his retirement in 1954, "The nearly 150 patents attributed to Harry Nyquist during his 37 years at Bell Laboratories merely suggest his contributions to the field of communications."

Analyzing the problem of maintaining stability in the negative-feedback amplifier invented by Harold S. Black, he produced what has been called the Nyquist Criterion (or the Nyquist Diagram) which defined the conditions required to keep the feedback circuits stable. This, wrote one of the circuit designers later, "was like a revelation on plates of gold. At last we knew what we were trying to achieve."* The diagram has also been used in the study of human regulating processes, even down to the manner in which a person steers an automobile.

Again, when J. B. Johnson discovered the thermal noise effect, he discussed it with Nyquist, who, Johnson himself wrote many

---

*A. C. Dickieson.

years later, "came up with the famous formula for the effect, based essentially on the thermodynamics of a telephone line, and covering almost all one needs to know about the thermal noise."[*]

"Nyquist," recalls one engineer now retired from Bell Laboratories, "had an almost uncanny ability to find the most direct and simple way to solve a problem. Many a time I have heard very intelligent people outline unique and elegant solutions. At the end Harry would say in his quiet way, 'Yes, that would surely do it, but have you considered this approach?'—at which point he would outline an almost simple-minded scheme that would be obviously far better."

It was Nyquist, also, who through theoretical analysis first determined the minimum band of frequencies required to transmit various kinds of communication signals. These studies laid one of the foundations for the development, years later, of information theory. In the television field, he invented a method of transmission used in TV broadcasting today and discovered a way to correct the distortion of television images that may be caused by some of the image-producing frequencies traveling faster than others. All in all, in his career at Bell Laboratories he combined, to a remarkable degree, talents for both theoretical analysis and practical invention.

---

[*]J. B. Johnson, "Electronic Noise: The First Two Decades," *IEEE Spectrum,* Vol. 8, No. 2 (February, 1971), pp. 42-46.

Rudolf Kompfner (left), inventor of the traveling wave tube, and Nyquist in 1960 discuss the theory of the tube.

accomplish as much or more that is right for the purpose at the right price by going farther down an *old* road than anyone else has gone before. So the idea is—let new and old compete; the more good options there are, the better the odds for making good choices. Multiple lines of development press the systems engineer to sharpen selective judgment.

QUANTITY PLUS QUALITY

While the multiplication of pathways may have been, as remarked above, the most striking aspect of transmission development, another change, gradual and imperceptible in most cases, has been equally important. To say it in one sentence, talking and hearing have been made much easier through the years, and standards for TV and data transmission have been set and held high.

The point here is not to dwell on the improvement. People today take good transmission for granted and have every right and reason to do so. It should not be thought, however, that this accomplishment has come by itself. It derives from a stream of developments, without which there could be no communications service as we know it. Circuits, for example, that enable talkers to talk without being confounded by the sound of their own voices in their ears. Devices that suppress echoes. Improvements in transmitters and receivers that reflect the discovery and artful organization of new materials in new instruments.

Behind good transmission are Harold Black's invention of negative feedback and all the associated mathematical research and refined circuitry that made distortion-free amplification possible. Behind it is the understanding of electrical noise, human physiology and basic communication theory that can guide good system design. Behind it, in the case of ocean cables, is the ability to put electronic repeaters on the ocean floor at pressures up to 7000

A special splicing vehicle designed by Bell Laboratories engineers connects two sections of millimeter waveguide, a new transmission medium that will initially carry 230,000 — and ultimately 460,000 — simultaneous telephone calls or an equivalent mix of voice, video and data signals. Splicing must be done with great care to minimize irregularities that interfere with wave transmission.

pounds per square inch with the firm expectation of uninterrupted performance—and the ability also to supply power to electronic gear through the entire length of the cable itself without affecting the circuits that carry speech. Behind it also, in the case of circuits that go via satellites in space, is the virtually noiseless amplification of currents so faint that the pressure of a rose petal on, say, Walden Pond would be strong in comparison.

The original problem in transmission was to make information intelligible over longer and longer distances. Now the distances are limitless and they

are also unpredictable—in the sense, for example, that a call destined for a point a thousand miles away may have to travel four times that distance over alternate routes if direct lines should chance to be busy. Also, the arts of carrier-system transmission require that in whatever form intelligence may be conveyed, it must undergo a really extraordinary amount of processing. Through all such transformations and vicissitudes, and over whatever distance, the signal must come clear at the end. Neither length nor breadth of circuit, nor the parallel existence of thousands of other signals, can be permitted to impair it. So, to repeat, the achievement of the transmission people has not been merely to create circuits by the million, but to produce high-grade, stable, dependable performance across the whole spectrum.

TRANSMISSION IS NOT ALL ELECTRONICS

It should also be said that there is more to transmission development than putting together better tubes, transistors, diodes and other circuit elements, remarkable as they all may be. There is a great multiplicity of other physical structures and these too go through an endless process of change and improvement.

Conventional telephone cables, for example, contained wire first insulated by wrappings of paper, then by paper pulp, then by films of polyethylene. Cable sheathing composed of a lead-antimony compound has given way to flexible layers of metal with an outer covering of polyethylene, and the life

continued on page 51

At Ligonier, Pa., Bell Laboratories and Western Electric engineers, at a field trial in 1974, check the terminal of a new electronic transmission system developed to improve rural telephone service. Using circuits that transmit many phone calls over two pairs of wires, the system provides single-party service to as many as forty customers simultaneously.

Claude Shannon

Creator of Information Theory

In 1948, Claude E. Shannon of Bell Laboratories published in the *Bell System Technical Journal* "The Mathematical Theory of Communication." Today information theory, as it is usually called, underlies all communications engineering. It is the subject of standard courses in major engineering colleges, the theme of learned studies around the world and the heart of a still-growing body of mathematical analysis.

When the layman asks, "What is information theory and what does it do for communications?" the engineer's answer is likely to be something like this:

Information theory provides a measure of what a communication channel can and cannot do. It enables us to quantify both the message source and the channel and relate them to each other. If the information rate exceeds the capacity of the channel (and both are measurable), then the communication will be subject to an amount of error that is also measurable. If the channel has more capacity than the information that is to be transmitted requires, then part of its capacity will be wasted—as would be the case, to give an extreme example, if a TV channel were used to carry only a voice. It is only by setting practical standards of fidelity and tailoring the system to meet them—and this usually entails accepting a degree of error that will either go unnoticed or may be economically rectified—that we can arrive at efficient systems. To have a trustworthy basic theory at hand to guide our effort is therefore of great value.

According to J. R. Pierce, formerly of Bell Laboratories and now professor of electrical engineering at California Institute of Technology, the heart of information theory is "the idea of source rate and deliberate, efficient encoding for transmission with negligible error over a channel of limited capacity."* And here it may be noted that while information theory is a general theory applicable to all forms of communication, the development of

---

*J. R. Pierce, "The Early Days of Information Theory," *IEEE Transactions on Information Theory*, Vol. IT-19 (January, 1973), pp. 3-8.

digital systems that handle information in streams of coded pulses provides an important method for putting its principles into practice.

Concerning the impact of information theory, Pierce has also written, "We expected knowledge . . . What some of us attained was perhaps wisdom rather than knowledge. Like the laws of thermodynamics, information theory divided a world into two parts—that which was possible and that which was not . . . Ingenious people no longer invented coding or modulation schemes that were analogous to perpetual motion. But, they were offered the possibility of efficient error-free transmission over noisy channels."

An interesting example of work benefiting from information theory is a system designed at Bell Laboratories for Picturephone transmission. The picture is encoded so that only what moves need be transmitted repeatedly as the motion occurs. Information on the background, which does not move, need be sent only once. Hence the channel does not have to have the capacity, or entail the cost, that would be required if the entire picture were repeatedly transmitted.

It should not be inferred, however, that information theory was solely responsible here. As Pierce points out, "The way we look at these forms of source encoding comes from information theory; the schemes themselves from human ingenuity."

The applicability of information theory to biology, psychology, linguistics and other fields has been, and continues to be, widely investigated. This need not concern us here except to note the continuing vitality and influence of Shannon's thought. In communications, information theory is perhaps best regarded as being, in his own words, "a valuable tool in providing fundamental insights into the nature of communications problems" although by no means, as he also observed, a panacea for the communications engineer.*

In 1952, Shannon devised an experiment to illustrate the capabilities of telephone relays. Here, an electrical mouse finds its way unerringly through a maze, guided by information "remembered" in the kind of switching relays used in dial telephone systems. Experiments with the mouse helped stimulate Bell Laboratories researchers to think of new ways to use the logical powers of computers for operations other than numerical calculation.

*C. E. Shannon, "The Bandwagon," *IEEE Transactions on Information Theory,* Vol. IT-2 (March, 1956), p. 3.

of this covering has been lengthened by antioxidant additives developed in the chemical laboratory. Nitrogen gas, dried air and jelly compounds pumped into cables have protected circuits against moisture. And where did that high-speed telegraph cable mentioned on page 29 acquire its talents? From an inner wrapping of permalloy, a remarkable magnetic alloy discovered way back in 1917 by G. W. Elmen of Western Electric's research department.

Better telephone instruments, together with the pulp-insulation process, have saved millions of tons of copper over the years by allowing use of fine-gauge wires for local transmission. The introduction of plastic sheathing—previously deemed impossible by industry—has cut the Bell System's consumption of lead, a relatively scarce metal, by two-thirds. Cables on the ocean floor have been protected against damage by trawlers through development and use of an almost unbelievable underwater plow which, pulled by a cable-laying ship, puts the cables *under* the ocean bottom in areas where trawlers work. These cables themselves, and in fact all coaxial cables, reflect Bell Laboratories and Western Electric designs and processes that have set standards for the cable industry worldwide—and the cable for the latest coaxial system, with its 22 coaxial conductors, is itself a new and delicate refinement.

Less complicated elements in the wide cross section of transmission development, but important nevertheless, are such items as a new, improved "drop" wire (from cable terminal to house) that may save a couple of million dollars a year; preformed manholes; plows that put wires underground without tearing up the landscape; and, for apartments and office buildings, interior cables that can be pulled into place more easily, and at less cost for labor, because their surfaces have been made a bit slippery. All such humble instances belong in the transmission story too, along with the transistor, network theory, luminescent diodes and whatnot, and while some

C. S. Long Lines, specially designed to install and repair ocean cables, returns to port after a voyage. *Long Lines'* primary assignment is to install the underwater cable links that carry telephone calls between the U.S. and countries overseas. The ship also repairs occasional damage caused by earthquakes and commercial fishing operations.

parts of the whole undoubtedly outweigh others, they all add up.

NEW DIRECTIONS

The prime influence of electronics on transmission, the reader must have noticed, has so far been in association with long-distance services. Distance has been conquered. Frequency bands have widened and widened again, creating a great network that can not only handle huge numbers of voice communications at remarkably low cost but also carry information in any form. Out of 500 million miles of voice channels in the nationwide long-distance system, all but one per cent are created by electronics; and *all* television, Picturephone, facsimile and high-speed data trans-

mission is possible only by reason of electronically derived pathways. Nor should we overlook the fact that direct distance dialing arrangements rely on the vast abundance of circuits available to handle calls over alternate paths as circumstances may require. The very flexibility of the network, and the ability

continued on page 55

An installation crew from AT&T's Long Lines Department lowers a section of coaxial cable into the Mississippi River south of St. Louis late in 1973. Coaxial carrier systems of this type have been designed by Bell Laboratories to carry up to 108,000 simultaneous telephone conversations —more than three times as many as the previous system. The cross-section view of the cable (inset) shows the 22 coaxial tubes.

Hendrik W. Bode

Mathematician, Physicist and Engineer

As we have seen, Harold Black's invention of negative feedback pointed the way to amplifiers that could strengthen long-distance telephone currents without distorting them and introducing unacceptable noise. Later Harry Nyquist produced the criterion— the Nyquist Diagram—that showed what had to be done to make feedback amplifiers stable; i.e., to keep them from "singing" when the current went through the feedback loop.

However, while the criterion established what had to be done, it did not tell how to do it. It was still up to the designers to meet the requirements, and to do so under more and more exacting conditions as the potential capacity of transmission systems increased. Many minds at Bell Laboratories attacked the problem. The most influential results were achieved by Hendrik W. Bode, whose book, *Network Analysis and Feedback Amplifier Design,* became the classic in the field.

In a talk about feedback years later, Bode pointed out the nature of the roadblock that had to be overcome and (rather diffidently) mentioned some of his own contributions.*

The first transcontinental telephone line, he remarked, used only a few repeaters (amplifiers) to overcome a loss of 60 decibels on a single channel. Twenty-five years later, a coaxial system that might handle 480 channels over a comparable distance would need 600 repeaters, or one every five miles or so, to overcome a loss of 30,000 decibels—500 times as much! And since the total noise and distortion that may be introduced by the repeaters— and must be prevented—is directly proportional to their number, it is necessary, as Bode put it, "for the individual components to become qualitatively better as the system as a whole becomes quantitatively more ambitious."

This made necessary some very exhaustive analysis. As it happened, Bode started by studying equalizers, which are circuit arrangements devised to compensate automatically for changes in temperature and other variants in transmission lines. Next, however, he had to find a way to put the equalizer into the feedback path without causing instability. This was a poser.

---

*Feedback — The History of an Idea, Brooklyn Polytechnic Institute, Proceedings of the Symposium on Active Networks and Feedback Systems, 1960.

"At length," Bode recalled, "in desperation, I began modifying the amplifier proper rather than trying to tinker further with my equalizer . . . Finally, after I had in effect redesigned the complete feedback loop, I found I could obtain a solution."

The experience exemplifies the often-repeated need at Bell Laboratories to dig deep for good answers. Bode for some years was a member of—and later headed—a group of mathematicians whose role was to bring mathematical theory to bear on pressing problems in physics, network design, probability and other areas. As his own achievement indicates, this interaction was extremely productive; indeed, Bode himself has emphasized that another Laboratories mathematician, L. A. MacColl, was instrumental in providing a basis for his own insights into the feedback problem.

Bode's insights, however, extended far beyond feedback design. He worked during World War II on electronic systems for gunfire control and, later, on problems in missile systems. After directing, in succession, both mathematical research and research in the physical sciences (his doctorate had been in physics), he became vice president of Bell Laboratories in charge of military systems engineering. Thus, as the heading of this note suggests, his career reflected an unusual combination of talents. After 41 years at the Laboratories he became, in 1967, Gordon McKay Professor of Systems Engineering at Harvard.

Not least among Bode's contributions at Bell Laboratories was his ability to put specific technical developments into a perspective suggesting their broader significance. For instance, in World War II he quickly understood the potential for changing the basis for weaponry control from mechanics to electronics and could organize work in the field within a broad logical framework. A second example may be taken from the talk already quoted.

The negative feedback devices used in telephony, he observed, must respond to randomly varying signals that are unpredictable except for the fact that they lie within a certain broad range. Similarly, he said, "The heart of communication engineering resides in the fact that we are dealing with the response of relatively complex systems to very complex ensembles of messages which are individually unpredictable but which can be dealt with in terms of some generally defining characteristics."

Thus in a few words Bode could define the overall problem, and at the same time point out a likeness between the feedback structure, and the whole of which it is a part, that somehow illuminates both the specific and the general.

Bode (right) confers with research mathematicians Sidney Darlington (left) and Henry O. Pollak in 1955. Among Bode's contributions as mathematician, physicist and engineer was his book, *Network Analysis and Feedback Amplifier Design,* which set forth the principles for designing transmission systems.

to manage it to respond promptly to shifting loads of demand, derive from its electronic versatility. Neither the speed nor the dependability of present-day communications would otherwise be possible. Moreover, were it not for the application of electronics to the communication network, it would be difficult if not impossible to find enough conductor material—notably copper—for today's needs.

Local exchange transmission, however, has not yet benefited from electronics in a comparable way. The reason has been economic, pure and simple: a pair of wires has generally been cheaper than the electronics that might take its place. What has been a cost-cutter over a thousand miles, or a hundred, has not been so over one mile, or two or three.

Will this situation continue? Not as in the past, surely. Already, as we have seen, digital electronic transmission systems are tying together central offices in metropolitan areas. And out in the country, too, things are beginning to change. Many long local lines in rural areas are already using semiconductor technology to advantage. New digital systems provide numerous circuits over a single pair of conductors. "Range extenders" improve transmission over fine-gauge wire. In an increasing number of instances, solid-state electronics can send two or more channels into a home, and do this economically, over one pair of wires. And off in the future—and it is a *reachable* future, Bell Laboratories people believe— is the prospect already touched on; that is, practical use, for all forms of communications, of the spectrum of light.

Finally, a word about what has been for many years transmission's stepchild. This is mobile communications. It has been around for years, yes, but in a limited way. This has been due mainly to the fact that radio frequencies have not been available to the telephone companies in quantity and, over fairly wide areas, only a few people could be served at a time.

Now, however, with the assignment of a wider band of frequencies for mobile service, Bell Laboratories has devised an entirely new system. Numerous low-power transmitters, each covering a relatively small area, would be able to serve many customers without interference. Whereas today mobile telephone users are still numbered in thousands, the new arrangements visualized would enable millions of people on the move to talk from telephones they carry with them. The wristwatch phone, it would appear, may no longer be an item for science fiction.

This system, by the way, relies on specially arranged electronic switching equipment that uses transistor technology. Again, therefore, we see the interdependence of transmission and switching, and how both, in today's communications art, reflect the impact of the semiconductor revolution.

Will there be more to come? Well, to close this chapter on a rising note, here are a few words from Eugene O'Neill, who directs Bell Laboratories' development work in long-distance transmission:

"I have to admit," he remarked, "that once or twice in the course of 30 years I've wondered what came next—whether we were reaching the end of the line or had wrung all the water out of the sponge. But I haven't felt that way for a long time now—a long time. I think the primary thing that has done it has been the transistor and the solid-state revolution. Once in a while I've been surprised to hear people much younger than myself worrying about coming to the end of the road, but I don't see any change in the rate of progress. . . If anything, you get the impression it is accelerating after all this time. Now you mention the optical thing. . ."

MICROWAVE RADIO:
A BRIEF CASE HISTORY

4

Starting in the late 1940's, towers supporting new kinds of antenna structures appeared in the land. From tower to tower, across distances averaging about 25 miles, radio waves ranging in frequency between 3.7 and 4.2 billion cycles per second carried voice and TV signals over six channels in each direction (one of them, however, a spare or protection channel). Each channel provided 480 voice circuits or could carry, alternatively, a television program.

A system of this kind was placed in service between New York and Chicago in 1950, and before the end of the following year a transcontinental system was in operation. From then on these systems grew in two ways: they covered more and more routes and they also increased in capacity.

What was behind this development? What was the system that spanned the continent composed of? What has been the history from then to now? Here is a partial answer:

Behind microwave radio, to begin with, was all the knowledge Bell Laboratories people had gained from their continuing study and design of vacuum tubes, wave filters, crystals, electrical networks, distortion-free amplifiers.

Behind it was the understanding of radio-wave propagation and reception acquired through the years by a research group led by Dr. Harald T. Friis. It was from their studies that the basic design of the new system emerged.

Behind it was intensive World War II experience in developing radar systems, which likewise use microwaves. This wartime experience, in turn, had built on Bell Laboratories' earlier development of microwave power sources; and it had also included development of a portable microwave communication system used by the Armed Forces in Europe and in the Pacific.

Behind it also, to name one more important source of know-how, were years of research on waveguides— tubular structures precisely fabricated to carry microwaves at ultrahigh frequencies. This waveguide

Standing atop 8300-foot Buckhorn Mountain in Colorado is a microwave radio relay station, one of the highest sites in the radio relay system. This network carries long-distance telephone calls, television programs and data throughout the United States.

technology, firmly based on mathematical and physical research, had been essential to radar systems and was no less essential now.

The system contained, then, among other things, and in addition to its towers and antennas:

1. The waveguides just mentioned. Their function: to carry microwaves from transmitters up to transmitting antennas, then down from receiving antennas to repeaters that amplify fading signals. Then up again go the rejuvenated signals, and on to the next relay station.

2. Complex electronic receiving, amplifying and retransmitting systems that first convert the received signals to lower frequencies (which can be amplified more easily), then strengthen the lower-frequency waves, then convert them back to their original frequencies and send them on their way.

3. As a pivotal element in the above, electron tube transmitters.

4. Crystal oscillators and filters that define and control all the frequencies in the system.

5. Equipment to effect instant automatic switching to the spare channel in case a working channel should fail.

6. Dehydrators to keep the waveguides bone-dry at all times. A detail, perhaps, but essential.

7. Power equipment. Test equipment. An emergency power source. And alarm systems to call the nearest control center.

These were some of the main elements in a system that could handle 2400 conversations over five working channels—480 per channel. But now let us see what has happened through the years.

Studying their handiwork, the engineers went to work to improve it. There was too much noise, they thought, in the "down converter"—the equipment that lowers the frequency in the amplifying system. So they

introduced another stage in the process and were also able to employ better crystals. The noise went down, more circuits could be handled, and by 1953 the 2400 circuits had increased to 3000.

The next change was even more fruitful. Getting ready to introduce a new system that would operate around six billion cycles a second, instead of four billion, development engineers contemplated using an antenna designed by Dr. Friis and his associates—the "horn reflector" antenna—that could handle waves oriented in space both vertically and horizontally. First, however, they decided to use it on the system already in service, whose six channels, carrying horizontal waves only, were separated by unused frequencies so that they would not bother each other. With the new antenna, these previously unemployed frequencies could now be used to carry waves vertically oriented— the vertical and horizontal would not interfere with each other—and the system could handle twice as many circuits: 6000 instead of 3000. This was around 1960.

Still not satisfied, the engineers worried about a difficulty being experienced in television transmission. Analyzing the problem, they made careful, detailed studies of the transmitter amplifying tube.

This astounding device, designed for microwave radio under the leadership of J. A. Morton, had already, it was thought, pushed the art of the three-element electron tube to its ultimate limits. Its electrodes were set closer together than vacuum-tube electrodes had ever been set before. Its grid required a thousand turns of almost invisible wires to the inch, and, to accomplish this, Bell Laboratories and Western Electric engineers had had to develop a remarkable winding machine. Now, however, renewed study of the tube showed that a minor change in the amplifier would resolve the television-transmission problem and would also permit operating the tube at double the power. So up went the number of circuits again, from 6000 to 9000.

By that time, in the mid-1960's, transistor technology was moving fast. A new semiconductor diode further

continued on page 62

Harald T. Friis

Moving Spirit of the "Old" Holmdel

Early in 1920, before Bell Laboratories was formed, a young man who had arrived in the United States a year earlier from Denmark was sent by his employer, Western Electric, to work in a small shack in Elberon, New Jersey. His desk consisted of a board over two packing cases and his job was to study and measure radio reception from ships.

From that day on, Harald Friis made a fair amount of history in radio research. He, and later a group that worked under his leadership, moved soon to a laboratory at nearby Cliffwood and later to Holmdel. There, at the "old" Holmdel lab, long before Bell Laboratories built a major installation in the same neighborhood, Friis and his associates set the course of major developments in radiotelephony, first in shortwave and later in microwave systems.

Friis had no sooner set foot in Elberon than he devised significant circuit improvements in the equipment he was to work with there. A couple of years later he produced, on hurry-up notice, the first superheterodyne broadcast radio receiver—the forerunner, actually, of present-day sets. Then followed, in succession, a receiver that would automatically compensate for fading signals, a more directional antenna, and methods for recording static and measuring shortwave signals as they faded. It was an antenna designed by Friis that Karl Jansky was using when he discovered the "star noise" that led to the science of radio astronomy (see page 107). In a memoir Friis wrote years later, after he had retired, he remarked, "Note that the inventions always originated because of a definite need."

The rhombic antenna, designed by Friis and Edmond Bruce,

found worldwide use in shortwave radiotelephony, which could hardly have been the same without it. Another system called MUSA (Multiple Unit Steerable Antenna) was not practical for general use but made it possible, in Friis' words, to unravel the phenomena of shortwave transmission. As has also been pointed out, electronically steerable antennas have recently become important in ballistic missile defense systems.

Moving on from shortwaves to microwaves, Friis and another associate, A. C. Beck, created the horn-reflector antenna now seen everywhere on microwave relay towers; and the Holmdel group as a whole investigated all aspects of microwave systems. By the time World War II started, in fact, they were quite prepared to go ahead with microwave transmission, for which the major components were by that time available. So it was that in 1947, soon after the war ended, AT&T was able to place the first experimental microwave relay system in operation.

Friis himself has said that his formula for radio transmission in free space, evolved in the 1930's but first published after World War II,* is his most important contribution. "This formula," his memoir says, "is used in designing the microwave communication system that now covers all of the U.S.A. The adjective simple has been applied several times, but the problems were actually not so simple before they had been solved."

Others have emphasized other aspects of Friis' strength. Ralph Bown, who was vice president for research at Bell Laboratories for several years, once said that Friis' notes told more about the conduct of research than all the books printed on the subject. John Pierce had the notes privately published under the title, "The Wisdom of Harald Friis," and added some interpretive comments of his own based on discussion with Friis. There is room here for just a few of the many ideas Friis brought together.

While big research projects might have to start with "the boss," he said, it is much better on small jobs to have the initiative come from the research worker. The boss's function is to help a

---

*"A Note on a Simple Transmission Formula," *Proceedings of the IRE*, Vol. 34 (May, 1946), pp. 254-6.

man do some clearly defined, worthwhile thing. The worker should be sure there is a real need and that the state of the art is ready for his effort. And if he is the right man for the job, it should haunt him day and night. If the importance of the job has decreased with time, or results are meager, it should be stopped.

One more thought, at the end of Friis' notes, can also end this sketch. The worker should remember, he said, that some credit belongs to the laboratory employing him; and in discussion with Pierce he modestly added, "The fact that I was planted in the Labs, and all the background, that was everything, John."

Friis (second from left) discusses an experimental circular waveguide with Bell Laboratories executives Ralph Bown (left) and Mervin J. Kelly in 1948.

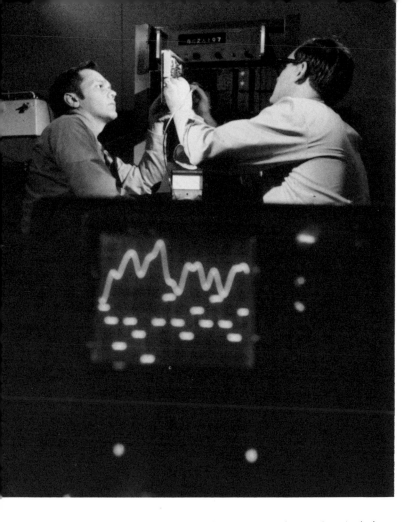

Bell Laboratories engineers test equipment for a technique called DUV (for Data Under Voice) which will provide new data-handling capabilities for the Bell System microwave radio network with only minor equipment additions. DUV allows high-speed transmission of information in digital form in the lower portion of the frequency band not always suitable for voice transmissions.

reduced noise in the receiver. A new solid-state amplifier was introduced in the down-converter mentioned above. New ceramic insulators replaced glass insulators in the transmitting tubes. Such changes made it possible to double tube power once again. And system capacity rose from 9000 circuits to 12,000.

So where do matters stand today? In 1973 the system had a capacity of 15,000 circuits and the engineers were working on a program to "retrofit" solid-state components into the system to improve reliability. They could meet reliability standards, they were sure, with only one spare or protection channel in 12, instead of one in six. Thus, with 11 working channels of 1500 circuits each, a total of 16,500 were in prospect.

Still the story is not told. What about that six-billion cycle system referred to above? The answer is that it too is alive and well and working hard—and on many routes, the same antennas you may have seen from the highway a few years ago, when they were handling only the four-billion cycle system, are now handling *both* the four and the six. Things may look the same, but they are not. In the buildings beside the towers, many elements—power, alarms, some waveguide runs and other components—are thriftily used in common for both systems, but many other elements are new. And to add up the circuits again . . . with the older system providing 16,500, and the newer providing eight channels (including a spare) of 1800 each, we are now up over 29,000.

But we have not quite finished. Soon, it is expected, solid-state technology will bring the six-billion cycle system up to 2100 circuits per channel, or 16,800 for eight channels, and *all* these, plus all 12 channels of the earlier system, can be used together to provide as many as 34,800 circuits over numerous routes.

But what about protection channels? Has the need for those been forgotten? No—and the explanation may surprise. These systems we have been discussing are long-haul systems for backbone routes. For other routes Bell Laboratories has developed other microwave systems, one of which operates around 11 billion cycles per second. In areas where there may be much rainfall, this must be used with care, for at that frequency communication signals may be affected by rain and amplifying stations may need to be only a few miles apart. However, Laboratories engineers have made very careful studies that show there is no

continued on page 66

Sergei A. Schelkunoff

George C. Southworth

Waveguide Experimenter and Waveguide Analyst

This book has referred several times to waveguides—both the circular waveguide for long-distance transmission of hundreds of thousands of conversations, and the rectangular pipes that guide microwaves in and out of radar equipment and through the receivers, amplifiers and transmitters of microwave radio relay systems.

The two scientists at Bell Laboratories most closely identified with creation of the waveguide technique were George C. Southworth and Sergei A. Schelkunoff.

It was Dr. Southworth who in 1931 began work at the Laboratories in waveguide transmission. This he undertook in the face of obstacles that had previously limited researchers to theoretical study. As early as 1897, Lord Rayleigh had proposed that radio waves could be propagated through hollow pipes or through rods made of insulating material, but no one had really tried to do it. One difficulty, for example, was that radio circuit designers, in order to exploit higher and higher frequencies, had already made the required coils and condensers about as small as possible—and waveguide transmission would reach into frequencies higher still.

However, from the work of Southworth and a small group of associates came discoveries of a fundamental kind. These covered not only the broad principle of transmission through pipes, but the possible function of the waveguide as an extremely directive antenna and, also, new arrangements that could take the place of the coils and condensers of ordinary radio practice. Together these advances established the basis for waveguide transmission.

In a 1936 article, Southworth told how his experimental research had been paralleled by work in mathematics, notably by J. R. Carson, Sallie P. Mead and Schelkunoff. "Sometimes experiment has suggested analysis," he said. "Sometimes analysis has suggested experiment." Waveguide history has strikingly demonstrated this. Depending on how the source of the wave is connected to the waveguide, many types of waves can be propagated. Particularly important, to continue Southworth's own account, was "the discovery that, theoretically at least, one of the many waves that may be transmitted through a hollow pipe becomes progressively less attenuated as its frequency is raised. This remarkable property appears altogether unique in the field of electrical transmission."*

---

*G. C. Southworth, "Electric Wave Guides," *Bell Laboratories Record,*
Vol. XIV, No. 9 (May, 1936), p. 285.

Schelkunoff studying waveguide transmission in the early 1930's.

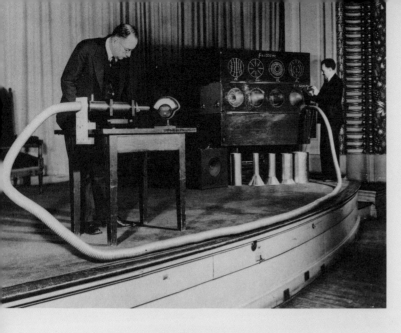

Southworth (left) in the first public demonstration of transmitting radio waves through a circular waveguide, in 1938.

Experiment has long since verified the theory. When the particular kind of wave Southworth referred to carries communications signals through a round waveguide, there is less degradation of the signal at an extremely high frequency (which permits handling many conversations simultaneously) than there would be at lower frequencies having less communications capacity. This is a fundamental reason why the long-distance waveguide becomes practical once the volume of communications that must be handled rises to very high levels.

As the name of Southworth is associated with experimental research in waveguide transmission, the name most strongly identified with mathematical theory in the field is that of Dr. Schelkunoff. Schelkunoff identified and defined the possible modes of transmission in various kinds of waveguides, provided the theoretical basis for their use in various radar and communication systems, and demonstrated mathematically the remarkable property referred to above; i.e., that the attenuation of a wave in the so-called circular mode is reduced as the transmission frequency is increased.

Southworth's studies led him also to the important discovery, announced in 1945, that the sun is a source of microwaves. Schelkunoff produced, in addition to his work on waveguides, much of the theoretical structure that underlies other wide areas of present-day radio. Just how far their complementary contributions to waveguide transmission will ultimately influence communications is still hard to say, but if a play on words may be excused, it looks as though they will make a lot of waves.

Bell Laboratories develops ways to use new technology in systems already at work in the Bell System. Here engineers test equipment that processes hundreds of voice and data channels for transmission over microwave radio or coaxial cable systems. The new units use less power and are smaller, less costly, more flexible and easier to maintain than their predecessors.

correlation between the times when rainfall may affect a rain-sensitive system and the occasions when another system may have to switch for a brief interval to a spare channel. Hence, it looks practical, in situations where all three systems may travel the same route, to put the protection channels on the third system and use the full capacity of the other two. Also, nowadays, with many alternate routes available, calls can quickly be routed around trouble spots.

DEVELOPMENT NEVER STOPS

The main theme of this brief synopsis has been the continuity of effort to appraise and improve performance. The gist of the matter is that development never stops.* Bell System microwave radio facilities today provide 358 million miles of long-distance telephone circuits—many more, in fact, than do cables, although that may change as time goes on. Had it not been for the microwave development, it is questionable whether public needs of the past 25 years could have been met. Also, while it is convenient to use telephone circuit mileage as a yardstick, it should be mentioned that most transmission of network TV programs is over microwave systems.

In the past decade or more, transistor technology has had increasing beneficial influence on microwave radio. However, as shown above, earlier technology has also been refined and improved. New and older arts have overlapped and both have been exploited and caused to work together. Today solid-state amplifier transmitters are in use in several systems; other systems are essentially solid-state but may use improved versions of vacuum-tube transmitters,† and others now under development are solid-state all the way. The new technology has had to prove itself costwise. Now that it is doing so, it offers overwhelming advantages in reliability and adaptability to future needs.

Here is another comment from Eugene O'Neill, the man in charge of long-distance transmission systems development. "We used to say," he remarked recently,

---

*Recent progress in microwave development may make it possible to include single-sideband transmission of amplitude-modulated (AM) signals [as compared to the present mode of frequency-modulated (FM) transmission] in radio systems. The use of single-sideband AM might eventually allow the Bell System to more than double the capacity of its microwave radio network.

†Another of these, in addition to the tube already described, is the *traveling-wave* tube invented in England in 1943 by Rudolf Kompfner, who joined Bell Laboratories a few years later. During a wartime visit to England, John R. Pierce of Bell Laboratories saw that this tube had great potential as an amplifier at ultrahigh frequencies. For several years Pierce, Kompfner and a group of associates worked to develop a rugged, reliable version.

Two Bell Laboratories engineers ascend a mast of an experimental radio relay system near the Laboratories' Merrimack Valley, Mass., location. In this system, streams of digital pulses at frequencies around 18 billion cycles per second will handle more than 28,000 phone calls simultaneously. The new system may be used in metropolitan areas to meet the growing demand for voice and data communications.

"that these solid-state devices were great but nobody could ever make microwave devices out of them. Well, the words were hardly out of our mouths when lo and behold, now we have not just one but several different kinds; and everybody hopes and expects that if we are able to apply the techniques used so successfully in the past, these things may last tens of years, 50 years, or more—whereas we used to be delighted to get five years from a vacuum tube."*

Finally, the microwave story offers a good example of how systems engineering—continuous analysis of objectives, opportunities, alternatives, needs, difficulties and results—helps development and design engineers to go after the problems that need solutions. That such teamwork will be needed just as much in future microwave radio development seems certain. For instance, radio in the still higher frequencies around 18 billion or even 30 billion cycles per second —the so-called millimeter-wave range—calls for digital (pulse) transmission and this demands very careful study of just how and where it may be used to best advantage. Perhaps digital radio systems can be used in metropolitan areas in the same way digital wire links already interconnect central offices. Perhaps they will be used to "feed" the 230,000-circuit waveguide, with which they are compatible. To get good answers to those and other questions, the systems engineers have some busy years ahead.

All in all, microwave radio is one of Bell Laboratories' major innovative contributions to communications, and the genesis, development, improvement and usefulness of these systems are a significant reflection of Bell Laboratories' usefulness in modern life.

*Tubes in telephone equipment placed on the ocean floor have lasted much longer, but at a cost not practical for other applications.

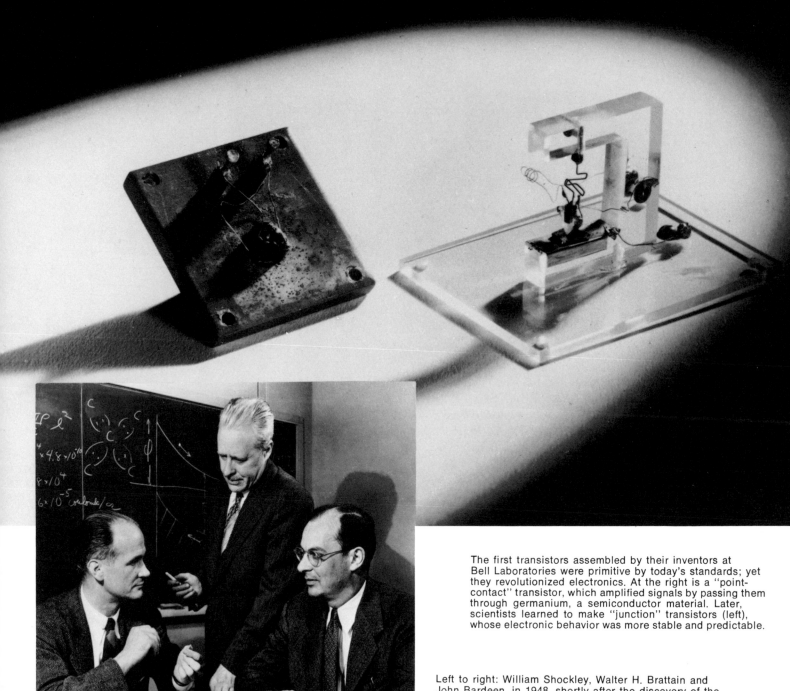

The first transistors assembled by their inventors at Bell Laboratories were primitive by today's standards; yet they revolutionized electronics. At the right is a "point-contact" transistor, which amplified signals by passing them through germanium, a semiconductor material. Later, scientists learned to make "junction" transistors (left), whose electronic behavior was more stable and predictable.

Left to right: William Shockley, Walter H. Brattain and John Bardeen, in 1948, shortly after the discovery of the transistor effect. In 1956 they were awarded the Nobel Prize in Physics for their work, a prime example of benefits from Bell Laboratories' mission-oriented basic research.

THE SOLID-STATE REVOLUTION

5

So much has already been written about the transistor that we shall repeat the generally known facts only briefly, for the record, and then suggest a few points that seem to belong with them.

The transistor was invented at Bell Laboratories by three physicists, John Bardeen, Walter Brattain and William Shockley, and the transistor effect—the amplification of a voice signal by a semiconductor crystal in an electrical circuit—was first observed there in December, 1947.

The invention resulted from intensive study of the nature of semiconductor materials, which are just what their name says they are—neither good conductors of electricity nor good insulators, but something in between. The first transistor employed a crystal of germanium. Subsequently, silicon has been the material most widely used.

Transistors can detect, amplify and rectify currents and switch them on and off. They are tiny, relatively cheap, and use very little power. Transistors and their cousins, the semiconductor diodes (which have two electrodes whereas transistors usually have three) can also be caused to produce electromagnetic waves of ultrahigh frequency, and in switching systems they can open or close circuits in millionths or even billionths of a second.

These various attributes have made it possible to develop electronic switching of communications and have likewise led to more efficient transmission systems on land, under the oceans, and through space —in fact there would be no satellite communications without transistors and diodes. Transistor technology has also made modern computers possible and enabled computers and communications to "talk the same language." Space flight, modern aeronautics, instruments of many kinds, industrial control systems, electronic guitars, heartbeat regulators, certain cameras, hearing aids, electronic watches, pocket calculators, and of course today's solid-state video, radio and hi-fi systems—all these and many other things depend on transistor art. The industries involved employ millions of people and their output worldwide amounts to many billions of dollars annually.

Most of the above has long been common knowledge. Some other aspects of the transistor story are perhaps not so widely understood.

First, invention of the transistor at Bell Laboratories was not a happy accident. It is true that such discovery

69

Semiconductor electronics have played a crucial role in making the computer revolution possible. Here, two Bell Laboratories employees use a computer to prepare an engineering drawing, directing the computer's graphic display with a "light pen" and monitoring the response on a screen. A wide variety of special and general purpose computers are used for research and development as well as business purposes at Bell Laboratories.

can never be predicted or depended on. However, a good deal was known about the behavior of semiconductor crystals in the 1920's and 1930's— the ability of a cat's whisker detector to detect radio waves, for example, and the ability also of some silicon crystals to convert light into electricity and even to change alternating current to direct current. Also, in these same years, it began to look as though the electron tube had been exploited almost to the limit. Indeed, for some purposes, in switching for example, it could not possibly be used to any great extent, for it consumed far too much power, produced far too much heat, and in any case could not be made in quantity, with the reliability required, at anything like a reasonable cost.

Could not an alternative be found, then, to the invaluable but nevertheless troublesome vacuum tube? And might not this alternative lie hidden in the remarkable, closely observed, but still mysterious behavior of semiconductors? Bell Laboratories management decided on an all-out effort to find the answer. This effort had to be deferred until World War II was over, but work started late in 1945 and met with success hardly more than two years later. Thus it was that a carefully planned program, stimulated by pressing need and conducted by scientists of exceptional ability, produced a discovery of enormous value.

The next point is that invention of the transistor was a beginning, not a conclusion, in more senses than one. A whole new technology had to be created: methods of fabrication, knowledge of the effect of design on performance, avenues to economical production. And requirements were stringent, for infinitesimal differences in subatomic composition—purity of materials, control of added elements—as well as protection of surfaces and stability of structure, made all the difference between go and no-go, between yes and no.

Step by step Bell Laboratories physicists, chemists

continued on page 73

John R. Pierce

Leader in Satellite Communications

John R. Pierce, the many-sided man who led the way to satellite communications, was initially moved to do so when preparing a talk for a meeting of the Princeton, New Jersey, section of the Institute of Radio Engineers in 1954.

"My topic was space," Pierce recalled later, "so I thought it would be interesting to make some calculations concerning the possibilities of communications satellites. I was astounded at the way things looked when I actually made the calculations."

This was three years before Russia launched the first Sputnik. With the subsequent rapid development of rocket power in the United States, Pierce pushed the idea of using a big plastic balloon, then being planned by the National Aeronautics and Space Administration to measure the density of the atmosphere at high altitudes, to reflect voice signals between transmitting and receiving stations in New Jersey and California. In 1960 the scheme was tried, with complete success.

This "passive" Echo satellite—so described because it did not actively retransmit the signals but merely reflected them—was followed in 1962 by AT&T's Telstar satellite, which had an amplifier-transmitter to relay the signals, and soon afterward by other active satellites.

Today satellite communication systems are vastly important in transoceanic service (more than 50 per cent of all the voice channels between the United States and other continents are obtained in this way) and domestic communication via satellite is both technically and economically practicable. A domestic satellite system should be in operation by 1976. The system will add 28,800 circuits to the long-distance network using satellites to be leased from the Communications Satellite Corporation.

Pierce made many other contributions during 35 years at Bell Laboratories. Important among them were ideas and designs for a device called the traveling-wave tube, which had been invented by Rudolf Kompfner in England in 1943. Years of work by Pierce, Kompfner and their associates at Bell Laboratories (which Kompfner joined in 1947) eventually made the tube into a powerful amplifier for microwave radio systems. It has also become a rugged, reliable component for communications satellites, which are, in effect, microwave relay stations in space. And here it should be said that Pierce's ideas about satellite communications went far beyond the Echo experiment, which he promoted simply as a practical, relatively inexpensive way to explore the possibilities. A technical paper he wrote in 1955, expanding his Princeton talk, covered all aspects of the subject and by the time of Echo he and others at Bell Laboratories had already carefully studied the resources developed there that might make active satellites economically useful. These included, beside the traveling-wave tube, the transistor; the solar battery; the horn-reflector antenna; an FM circuit invented at Bell Laboratories many years earlier; and an extremely low-noise amplifier, the maser, that introduced only about one one-hundredth as much noise as previous amplifiers.

Pierce also invented the helical structure for the inner wall of the circular waveguide. For years he directed research programs in electronics and in communications systems and principles, including studies in mathematics, acoustics, vision, economic analysis and psychology. Numerous other inventions resulted in 88 patents. Pierce was also a writer (13 books and a lot of science fiction while he was at Bell Laboratories), a wit ("Nature," he once said, "abhors a vacuum tube") and above all a stimulator of other people. When he retired from the Bell System in 1971 to teach at California Institute of Technology, President Baker of Bell Laboratories (at that time vice president for research) said, "John Pierce has unwaveringly looked for the most challenging ideas that science and engineering could contain. He often personally phrased these in forms which excited the best energies and enthusiasm of whole generations of collaborators."

It was this capability that made Pierce, more than any other man, responsible for bringing satellite communications from dream to reality.

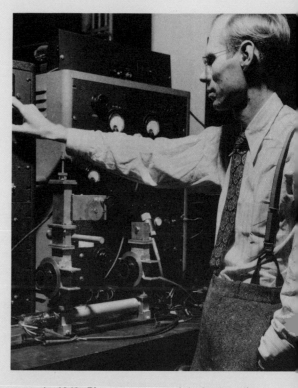

In 1949, Pierce tests a model of a traveling wave tube, one of several Bell Laboratories developments that made satellite communications possible.

and metallurgists evolved the basic processes on which all transistor production depends. Morgan Sparks made the first "junction" transistor, which could be operated, as foreseen, on a millionth of a watt. G. K. Teal and Ernest Buehler learned to grow single crystals of silicon. William G. Pfann invented a refining process that could produce uniform crystal ingots with only one atom in ten billion out of line (a purity that has been likened to 38 carloads of sugar with a single pinch of salt). G. L. Pearson, C. S. Fuller and D. M. Chapin, using strips of silicon, invented the solar battery, the first device that could successfully convert useful amounts of the sun's energy directly into electricity. C. S. Fuller developed a technique for diffusing minute quantities of other materials into semiconductor crystals, in order to create the junctions of positive and negative charge on which transistor action depends; and other workers later developed methods to improve control over the diffusion process. O. L. Anderson, Howard Christensen and Peter Andreatch devised the "thermo-compression" technique for bonding metals with semiconductor crystals. Still other workers in the transistor vineyard developed a method for growing, on a silicon crystal surface, silicon films identical in structure with the crystal itself; this *epitaxial* process, so called, made possible silicon transistors that operated ten times as fast as any made before.

More detail could become tedious. The reason for mentioning the above instances is simply to suggest the kind of team effort, bringing theory and experiment together, that had to be made in order to realize the transistor's promise.

Furthermore, all this work, and more beside, was itself but a beginning, a start down the road toward integrated circuitry. There is hardly a man, woman or child today able to read or look at a picture who has not learned that umpteen thousands of indiscernible transistors and diodes can be woven into fabulous mazes of circuitry hardly wider in diameter than an infant's fingernail. Here again, to make a long story very short, Bell Laboratories development teams (in teamwork also with Western Electric manufacturing engineers) made basic steps forward in the designs and

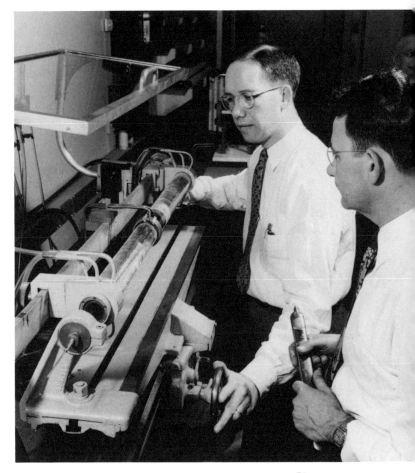

Inventor W. G. Pfann (left) demonstrates his "zone-melting" technique for refining semiconductors to an impurity concentration of one harmful atom in ten billion atoms of the material. J. H. Scaff, a pioneer in semiconductors, stands at right. Pfann's invention paved the way for mass production and widespread use of transistors.

In 1964, Bell Laboratories scientists invented a solid-state device, known as the IMPATT diode, ultimately able to produce 100 milliwatts of power at frequencies up to 110 billion cycles per second. The diode can generate high-frequency waves that will carry information through the high-capacity millimeter waveguide system.

processes that give integrated circuits their remarkable characteristics and capabilities.

A third important beginning was prompt action to tell the world what was going on. As soon as a reliable body of knowledge was available, Bell Laboratories moved to inform the government, other industries and the universities about the developing transistor technology. This was accomplished through symposia and demonstrations as well as through publication. In this connection, a comment made in 1961 by P. E. Haggerty, then president of Texas Instruments, bears quoting.

"As a concrete illustration of how rapidly new knowledge can affect our society usefully, and, in the process, generate enormous support for more good science," Mr. Haggerty wrote, "I can think of no better illustration than progress in the general field of semiconductors since the Bell Telephone Laboratories Spring, 1952, symposium in which their new

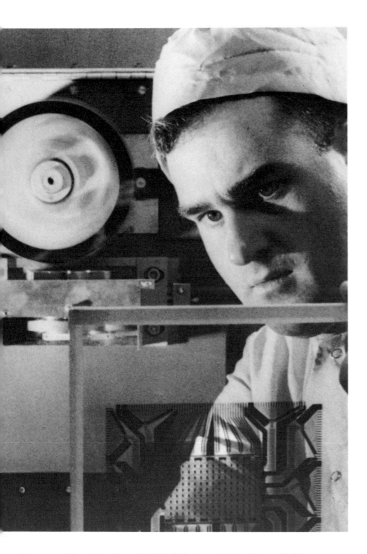

knowledge was made available in a systematic and organized manner . . . ."

One other beginning may just possibly have more meaning for the future than any other. Discovery of the transistor effect threw a new light on the behavior of electricity in solid materials, or, to say it differently, on how energy may function in solids. Much has already been learned about changes in energy levels, the effects of pressure and temperature, crystal dislocations and many other things. These are further indicators that the solid world we walk on seems to have even more subtle and remarkable powers still awaiting analysis.

So the transistor has stimulated a new awareness of the potentials of solids and, finally, a new emphasis on solid-state physics in the universities. It is interesting to reflect that these beginnings, no less than those demanded for the creation of semiconductor technology, have come about because the Bell System had a need.

In a machine developed at Bell Laboratories, laser light draws intricate patterns for masks or templates used in the manufacture of integrated circuits. The machine, which can accurately generate very complex masks in minutes, is used by Western Electric in producing circuits for an increasingly wide variety of telephone equipment.

Semiconductor devices depend on "doping"—introducing minute amounts of another material in a semiconductor to achieve desired electrical properties. Here, scientists test a new doping technique called "ion implantation," in which the semiconductor is bombarded by high-speed charged particles, or ions, of the desired material. Ion implantation is used by Western Electric to fabricate semiconductor devices that require very precise doping.

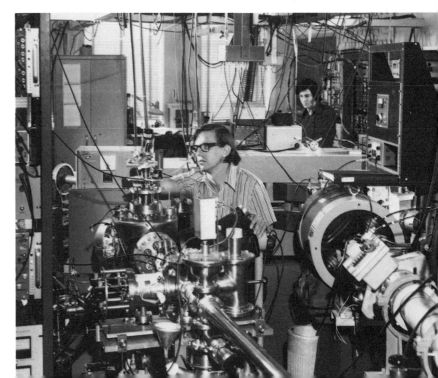

Telephone company employees in Trenton, N.J., work at control consoles (left) and in bays of equipment that make up one of the largest No. 1 Electronic Switching Systems (ESS) in the Bell System. No. 1 ESS was designed for service in cities and large suburbs. The application of solid-state electronics and stored-program control to telephone switching is the largest Bell System development project ever undertaken by Bell Laboratories.

SWITCHING – THE ENDLESS CHALLENGE

6

Total interconnectedness is the unique distinguishing attribute of network telecommunications—its triumph—and an endless puzzlement, also, to engineers as both the network and its uses continue to grow.

It may be of interest, instead of starting at the beginning, to look first at a few up-to-the-minute Bell Laboratories developments to see what is involved in present-day interconnection, and let the backward look follow.

Exhibit A will be a machine the engineers have tagged No. 4 ESS, the letters standing for Electronic Switching System. The first of these is being installed in Chicago to switch long-distance calls and data communications. The central portion of this system, using solid-state technology, resembles a digital computer, having memory, logic and stored programs, although completely different from general-purpose computers.

No. 4 ESS directs calls toward their destinations— makes connections—by *time-division* switching, whereby coded pulses carrying each call are placed in time slots, in millionths of a second, under control

of solid-state logic circuitry.* The machine can handle over 350,000 calls an hour, switching them to and from 100,000 terminals. Taking into consideration the average length of time that conversations are held, this means putting up and taking down about 100 connections per second. In comparative terms, No. 4 ESS has about three times the capacity of present-day long-distance switching machines and can serve nearly five times as many trunk lines.

FIRST OF MANY

The Chicago machine is scheduled to start working in 1976. It will be the first of many. Plans call for two more in 1976, then 11 more in 1977, then about 20 a year thereafter. And some or all of the later machines may each be three times larger than the first one.

Is a machine with the power of No. 4 ESS really necessary? If it were not so considered, it would not be contemplated. Let it be remembered that long-distance telephone communications have more than

---

*The first commercial application of time-division stored-program control to switching, in 1963, was in an electronic private branch exchange (PBX) system developed at Bell Laboratories.

quadrupled within the last 18 years and that intercity data communications in the past few years have grown at a faster rate than long-distance calling volumes. And these rates of growth are continuing. Much of the data traffic is still specially handled, but it is not difficult to foresee great increases in data communications over the nationwide switched network. Bell engineers point out also that the circular waveguide, with its tremendous call-carrying capacity, will soon be making its way across the land; to switch the total volume of communications that can be transmitted through a single waveguide, no fewer than three No. 4 ESS machines would be required.

What about costs? And why is this machine designed as it is to switch digital pulses by slotting them in time? The questions go together. The answers lie largely in the compatibility of digital *time-division* switching with Pulse-Code Modulation transmission. As noted elsewhere, PCM has already made great strides and for compelling reasons is bound to make more. When both transmission and switching function digitally, the interface is relatively simple and can be supplied at very low cost.

In addition, however, a No. 4 ESS machine, while doing three to five times as much work as its predecessor, occupies hardly more than a tenth as much expensive real estate and uses much less electrical energy per connection. For this reason as well as others, a machine like the one in Chicago can also switch analog currents—even though they require conversion to PCM before they go through the switching process—more economically than the present long-distance machines.

Here is another interesting new development in switching:

EVEN FASTER CONNECTIONS

When you make a long-distance call, your local switching machine finds an idle trunk line and sends the signaling pulses for the number you want on their merry way. But if the called phone is busy or does not answer, the trunk has been tied up to no purpose except to find that out. A new method, to be applied first on some routes in 1976, uses a high-speed data channel, linking stored-program electronic processors at both ends, to carry many number pulses —yours and other people's—simultaneously. In other words, there is one signaling channel common to a lot of trunks. This Common Channel Interoffice Signaling (CCIS) enables the switching machines to learn everything they need to know about the call *before* the talking path is set up. Another potential money-saver, this also uses solid-state technology.

CCIS also has some other talents. For example, suppose a call from Europe to Japan goes part of the way over a circuit that travels 22,300 miles up to a communications satellite in space and an equal distance down again to an earth station in the United States; from there it must be sent on to its destination

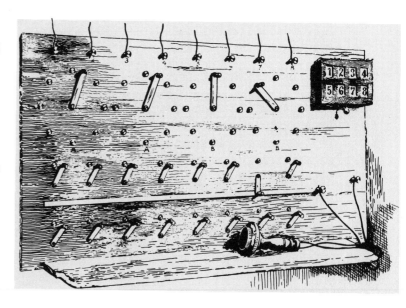

The first telephone switchboard, installed in New Haven, Conn., 1878. Telephones were connected by rotating the metal arms to various electrical contacts in the wooden panel. Notice the operator's "telephone."

across the Pacific. Already its trip has taken six-tenths of a second. If it goes the rest of the way by means of another satellite relay, that will take another six-tenths and this will be entirely too much; the accumulated delay would confuse the people at both ends of the line and make conversation well-nigh impossible. CCIS, however, will prevent this. How? By including, in such a case, a code which in effect says to the switch in the United States, "This call is already planned to proceed over one satellite link. Do not send it on to Japan over another."

This description may sound as though CCIS uses up considerable time. The contrary is true. Today it takes perhaps 12 seconds or more to complete a direct-dialed long-distance call after the call has been dialed. The objective for CCIS is that 95 per cent of all calls will take less than one second. This will be especially useful, by the way, in the switching of data calls, many of which are very short; where computers are involved, speed in setting up connections is important to their efficient use.

Now to step backward a little in time:

BEGINNINGS OF ELECTRONIC SWITCHING

Ahead of No. 4 ESS came, in 1965, after about ten years of development work, the first No. 1 ESS. It was the first production-model electronic central office switching system in the world to use a stored memory/logic program. Also to be mentioned are No. 2 ESS (for use in suburbs) and No. 3 ESS (for use in rural areas), which with No. 1 make up a family of systems of different sizes—the Three Bears, one might say, of local-exchange electronic switching in the Bell System. At this point, however, leaving code numbers and such behind, let us briefly sketch the overall development of electronic switching, its impact and Bell Laboratories' role.

It all began, to put it simply, with the transistor. Back in the 1930's, before World War II, there had been some research at Bell Laboratories toward applying electronics to switching. (After all, hadn't the vacuum

A trouble-shooting session is in progress at Bell Laboratories in Indian Hill, Ill., on a developmental version of the new No. 4 Electronic Switching System (ESS) for tandem and toll switching. No. 4 ESS, scheduled for commercial service in 1976, will help the Bell System handle economically the heavy communications traffic of the future.

tube worked wonders in transmission?) But nothing came of it. Too much power needed, too much heat generated, too little else. "But the transistor changed the whole business"—that is how W. H. C. Higgins, who had charge of switching development at the Laboratories until his retirement in 1973, expresses it. "This thing was reliable, fast and worked on low power. We started development around 1954 and it turned out to be the biggest job ever."

Two questions are natural. Why electronic switching at all? And has it been worth it?

ADVANTAGES

The essential advantage inherent in the electron, for control of switching, is its speed. All previous automatic switching equipment has been controlled electromechanically, with relays (switches) setting up pathways through networks of possible contact points. Much of this control equipment is extremely sophisticated: modern crossbar systems, in particular, reflect concepts that give them almost dazzling capabilities. Electromechanical control apparatus, however, cannot move in millionths of a

second and this limits what it can do. The equipment also takes up a good deal of room. It does not contain stored programs in the same sense as the program of an electronic system. So, generally, if the function of the system is to be altered, or some new feature added, the physical configuration of the control hardware must be changed. Installations and changes require much labor and, while a lot has been done through the years to make crossbar equipment more efficient (most recently with the help of mini-computers and centralized maintenance systems), high labor costs strengthen the conclusion that there are limits to what more can be accomplished to hold down installation charges and maintenance expense.

Electronic switching, however, presents a quite different outlook. A stored program is possible and practical. Billions of bits of information are compactly stored in the memory, and semiconductor circuitry allows almost instant access, retrieval and logic functions. Every Bell-designed ESS is in fact like a computer—quite different, to repeat, from general-purpose computers but much like a computer nonetheless. And as in the case of other computers, the program, the software, can usually be changed without changing the hardware.

With regard to electronic central office costs, Bell Laboratories engineers say: "Electromechanical crossbar equipment is still a tough competitor if you consider initial investment alone. However, the capabilities of electronic systems are steadily increasing and, at the same time, production economies are being achieved as the volume of production increases. Also, we have a lot of new integrated-circuit technology and new magnetic devices going into the newest systems and this is starting to affect costs

Switchboards in 1883, with operators seated on wooden chairs, were separated by panels known as "annunciator drops" between operator positions. These annunciator drops gave visual indications of telephone lines requesting service.

favorably. But aside from first costs, we have to take maintenance costs into account and already the maintenance costs of electronic systems, by and large, are approaching half of what it costs to maintain crossbar equipment."

Another important factor is the adaptability of electronic offices to system changes and new features that may yield economies, improve service, or both.

SPECIAL FEATURES

"For instance," the engineers explain, "we now have a new system, also electronic, that will automatically intercept calls made to numbers that have been changed, and give the calling customer the new number by means of a computer-controlled assembly of recorded numbers and phrases. This Automatic Intercept System (AIS) saves the services of three out of every four operators otherwise needed for this particular job. (Some operators are retained in case customers from time to time want to ask questions.)

"Now, to connect AIS into a group of crossbar exchanges requires making equipment changes at a cost of about $12,000 in each exchange. To hook AIS up with an electronic exchange, however, we need only modify the exchange's stored program; and this is easily done by putting a few hundred words, in computer language, into the program over a teletypewriter circuit."

Electronic switching offers other advantages, too. It is relatively easy to provide special features—for instance, to indicate to a person who is using the telephone that another call is waiting; to forward incoming calls automatically to another telephone; to reach frequently called numbers by dialing only three or four digits. Also, and this is extremely important, electronic switching techniques greatly improve the efficiency of operator services. When these are provided in conjunction with electronic systems, only two operators are needed for every four who would

In the 1930's, when telephone engineers developed the crossbar switch (banks of which are seen above, left), they greatly expanded the "brain power" of switching equipment. Crossbar systems have common control circuits more powerful than earlier switching systems. These circuits receive and memorize each called number, select a route for the call through the switching system, and seek alternate routes if the primary path is busy.

otherwise be required. The aggregate saving in labor costs is very large.

This is not, of course, a contribution to unemployment. It is one more in the series of steps that have kept the cost of electrical communications at levels that invite increasing use and so enhance employment opportunities. Without the development of automatic switching for both local and long-distance service, for example, telephony would long since have been swamped by the rising tide of labor costs. The use of electronic systems to aid the handling of calls that still require the services of telephone operators is desirable for similar reasons—in addition to the fact that calls can be completed faster.

To look at the development of direct distance dialing, we shall take, in a moment, another step backward in time. First, however, these conclusions on the present:

ELECTRONIC SWITCHING HAD TO COME

From the time the transistor appeared, the application of electronics to switching was inevitable. The capacity for near-instant memory retrieval and logic had to be applied to the communications network. The challenge to the developers was staggering, the programming difficulties greater than had been anticipated, and the costs higher also. Already, however, as suggested above, costs are in good balance

Semiautomatic switching of telephone calls was tried in Newark, N.J., in 1915, using the switchboard in the foreground. A customer gave the desired number to one of the operators, who then dialed the party's number. If the call was not local, an operator in a distant office would be dialed. This and subsequent tests indicated that fully automatic switching of phone calls would be simple and economical.

with electromechanical equipment; maintenance is far less expensive and first costs are coming to the crossover point. Features not otherwise practical are easily provided and operational savings are large and growing. In the case of No. 4 ESS, with which this chapter started, the functions to be performed could not be performed at all by other than electronic means. This is another way of saying that the marriage of digital transmission and long-distance digital switching systems, as now foreseen, could not otherwise have been contemplated.

It may be asked whether time-division switching like that embodied in No. 4 ESS is used also in local electronic exchanges. So far it has not been. Small magnetic reeds that open and close contacts under the control of transistor logic compose the switching network in local ESS exchanges. In the newest systems the reeds themselves, now made of a Bell Laboratories-discovered alloy called *remendur,* have been completely redesigned. They take about a quarter as much room as the reeds they replace, operate on low power supplied through solid-state devices, are prewired and tested at the factory and cost a third less. This is another reminder that development effort never ends. It also strengthens the present feeling at the Laboratories that, for local exchanges, space-division switching still offers controlling advantages.

Development engineers point out, for example, that the devices used for digital time-division switching are not well suited to work with some of the electrical currents now needed in the local exchange. But the major problem centers in the cost of converting into pulses the waves produced by the human voice. These costs, as we have seen, are eminently practical for the new high-capacity long-distance switching machines, and in creating numerous digital circuits over single pairs of wires. Indeed, carrier systems that rely on wave-to-pulse converters are now employed not only on lines interconnecting central offices, but on some of the longer local lines

The massive task of providing electrical connections between customers' telephones and a central office's switching equipment, a function sometimes plagued by overcrowding of wires and by record-keeping problems, is yielding to solutions devised by Bell Laboratories engineers. The connecting frames pictured here are part of a system that brings modern design, computer-aided record keeping, and new administrative techniques to this essential job.

running back to customers' telephones. Not yet, however, is the cost of conversion low enough to allow the general use of digital, time-division switching in local exchanges.

Does this mean, perhaps, not yet . . . but soon . . . or some day? That is a leading question that different engineers will answer in different ways. But most agree that the future depends in great measure on progress in the large-scale integration of solid-state circuits. There lies an essential key to lower-cost converters, and possible further radical change in the switching art.*

Finally, with respect to stored-program electronic switching, it seems clear that this is the wave of the future worldwide. It is also clear that the United States

is well out in front. At the beginning of 1974 the Bell System was serving 5.6 million customer lines, or nine per cent of the total, through 475 electronic central offices. Some 200 electromechanical systems serving about 2 million lines were replaced by electronic systems in 1974, and the prospect for 1985 is that about 50 per cent of all Bell System customers will be connected through electronic exchanges in 4700 ESS offices in communities large and small.† All this in the years since the first No. 1 ESS was placed in operation in Succasunna, New Jersey, in 1965. And, in the interval, performance has become steadily more dependable; in 1973, for example, the total

---

*In a talk a few years ago by John R. Pierce, some of whose work at Bell Laboratories is sketched on page 71, Pierce remarked, "I feel confident that better and cheaper and very reliable integrated circuits will lead to new concepts in switching and that switching costs as well as transmission costs will come down drastically."

---

†Elsewhere in the world, latest available figures (end of 1972) indicate that there were only 16 electronic central offices in operation, with a total capacity of fewer than 100,000 lines.

An engineer at Bell Laboratories in Indian Hill, Ill., checks operation of new control equipment for electronic switching systems. The new unit, called a "processor," uses solid-state circuits to control switching of phone calls faster and more dependably than its predecessors. The new unit is also easier to maintain, takes less space and needs less power.

accumulated "downtime" in 450 Bell System electronic exchanges (which automatically restore themselves to operation, in case of failure, by cutting over almost at once to standby equipment) averaged 13 minutes per office for the year—a downtime that in most offices usually affected relatively few telephones for a few minutes, or a few seconds, at a time.

With telecommunications growing year after year, it is difficult to see how, without ongoing developments such as electronic switching, interconnection facilities adequate to the long-range future needs of society could be provided. Also, it is no more than fact to say, first, that the search for something like the transistor—something that would allow low-power, dependable control of electron behavior in switching systems—originated at Bell Laboratories; that

discovery and fundamental development came to pass at Bell Laboratories; and that the development of electronic, stored-program switching systems likewise began at Bell Laboratories and has there been brought to successful and increasingly efficient performance.

DIRECT DISTANCE DIALING

Many people nowadays probably cannot remember the day when they were not able to dial a long-distance call. For their elders, however, no change in telephone service was more noticeable at the time it occurred. And for everyone who makes some of the 7.7 billion long-distance calls that are being dialed directly in the United States this year, no change has done more to promote speed and economy of service than Direct Distance Dialing—DDD.

As early as the 1930's, some calls were being dialed between cities and towns within relatively small areas, both in the United States and in Europe. However, to provide a uniform DDD service that would automatically interconnect increasing millions of users through thousands of switching centers spread across the length and breadth of most of North America—this was something else again. The plan to accomplish the job was developed jointly by AT&T and Bell Laboratories engineers; the latter established the technical requirements and developed the switching and associated systems needed for uniform 10-digit dialing* and accurate accounting.

This was an evolutionary process. It began with telephone operators dialing calls straight through to the distant telephone, first in a few cities, then over widening areas. The first community in which telephone users could dial calls directly to certain far-distant points was Englewood, New Jersey. This was in 1951. Five years later 11 million customers could dial nearby cities and towns and more than 2½

---

*In some areas one additional preliminary digit may be needed but most customers dial only ten.

million could dial over the longer routes. By 1965 nine out of ten telephones were able to use DDD and today this service is well-nigh universal.

To provide such service, the first and fundamental need was for a concept and numbering plan that could be applied nationwide, and for switching arrangements that could produce a uniform service notwithstanding the wide variety of local dial systems used by different telephone companies, both Bell and Independent, all over the country. Or to put it another way, the long-distance switching equipment had to be able, figuratively speaking, to *understand* the nature and characteristics of different local systems so that it could, literally, *translate* different inputs into a common language that would be understood at all intermediate and terminal points.

To accomplish this, Bell Laboratories designed types of crossbar switching systems that were considerably more sophisticated than anything that had been attempted before. As an example of their capabilities, consider a coast-to-coast call that is dialed at a moment when, as might happen, all direct circuits are busy. The machine we are discussing learns this at once when it seeks to comply with the first three digits, and immediately signals, let us say Chicago, in quest of an alternate route. The Chicago machine checks the first three digits in turn and if it has a route clear to the destination area, it sends the other seven digits on. However, if it does not have a direct route available over the rest of the distance, it checks again and might now send all ten digits to St. Louis, where another machine looks the situation over and decides whether it can forward the call directly or must try another switching point. And so on.

Another necessity for DDD was a method of keeping track of who calls where, at what time, and for how long. To meet this need Bell Laboratories developed an Automatic Message Accounting (AMA) system to record and process the information on wide

Engineers from Bell Laboratories, Western Electric and Illinois Bell Telephone Company run through operational checks on a No. 2 Electronic Switching System (ESS) installed in Oswego, Ill., in 1970. No. 2 ESS was designed by Bell Laboratories engineers to supply the advantages of electronic switching to rural and small suburban communities.

paper tapes. This was a wonder of its time and a step toward the improved magnetic tape recording systems that are now superseding it.

No less essential to the success of DDD was the development of new methods of signaling. When operators started to dial calls straight through to the distant telephone, this was quite a different matter from signaling between switchboards. For customer dialing, with no operator involved, a further radical change in the signaling system was required.

Traffic Service Position System (TSPS) consoles, introduced in 1969, at the Englewood, N.J., office of New Jersey Bell. With electronic processing of phone calls controlled by programmed instructions, TSPS provides lower cost, faster service on operator-handled calls and more effective means for detecting problems in the telephone network.

Finally, DDD depended on the ready availability of circuits over alternate paths. The pathways had to be there in great numbers. In other words, the success of *transmission* technology in providing thousands of circuits at low cost was essential to this tremendous change in *switching,* and again we see the interdependence of the two.

To sum up at this point, five imperatives had to be met in order to accomplish direct distance dialing.

These were, first, a plan, both specific and complete, to harmonize local and long-distance systems in the interest of a uniform service; second, a reliable automatic accounting system; third, new signaling techniques; fourth, an abundance of transmission paths; and fifth, new long-distance switching equipment that would accept, smoothly translate, and promptly deliver signals to and from a great diversity of terminal apparatus all over the country. All this has been accomplished, although the system is continuously being refined and, as we have seen, a transition toward the marriage of digital transmission and digital electronic long-distance switching is already under way.

CONCEPTS AND FOUNDATIONS

One reason for having lingered a bit on the subject of DDD is that it offers a prime example of close, continuing collaboration among Bell Laboratories and telephone company people.* Another reason is that this whole development brings out clearly the advantages inherent in the principles of *translation* and *common control*. These have been the foundations of Bell Laboratories' contributions to switching technology and it was only on these foundations that uniform nationwide dialing could have been structured.

The same principles, however, strongly influenced the entire development of switching in the United States long before DDD was dreamed of. As noted elsewhere in this book, the first automatic systems were composed of switching trains that operated

continued on page 90

*To this it might be added that such collaboration also involves Western Electric to a high degree, not only in producing equipment but in installing it. For instance, it was noted at the AT&T annual meeting in 1959 that when a long-distance switching machine was being installed in Wilmington, Delaware, Western Electric installers were also at work in 57 other exchanges that were about to be connected with the Wilmington equipment. The need was to modify local apparatus in these communities on a precise schedule pointing toward a certain date. It was noted also, on the same occasion, that such work was facilitated by the fact that Western's records showed the exact location of every piece of equipment in each exchange and where every wire terminated.

Edward C. Molina

Pioneer in Telephone Switching Theory

"The early development and application of probability theory to telephony in America is largely a recitation of the contributions of E. C. Molina," says a biographical sketch written by an admiring associate at Bell Laboratories.*

Probability theory has been important in telephony for the reason that it is necessary to provide enough equipment, in efficient configurations, to handle expected volumes of calls, but economically wasteful to provide more. Molina, whose work in the field elicited the comment above, was a self-taught mathematician and circuit designer who never went to college. He joined the research department of AT&T in Boston in 1901 and only a few years later proposed a procedure for telephone switching that solved a basic problem and still stands as one of the underlying concepts of the switching art.

The problem was this: Early step-by-step automatic switches operated entirely on the decimal system. Not only did customers dial numbers between one and ten, as they do today, but the switching contacts and the lines interconnecting successive switches were likewise arranged in tens. Early probability studies showed, however, that switching would be much more efficient

*R. I. Wilkinson, "The Beginnings of Switching Theory in United States," *Electrical Engineering,* Vol. 75 (September, 1956), pp. 796-802.

if switches and lines could be used in larger groups. Yet it seemed most unlikely that nondecimal dialing could ever be made to work—there would be too many errors.

Molina thereupon invented a method of *translation* to convert the dial pulses from decimal to nondecimal form. People could still dial the same way, but the switches and trunk lines were freed from dependence on the decimal number plan and the way was open for development of far more flexible, efficient switching systems.

More than 40 years later Thornton C. Fry, a Bell Laboratories mathematician who at the time of his writing was director of switching research and engineering, appraised Molina's invention of translation as "one of the great basic inventions of our time."

Fry said of the translator, "It completely freed the automatic mechanisms which connect telephone subscribers together from slavish dependence on the decimal system. It would be hard to estimate how much money this has saved, but it would be very large. Conversely, it freed the subscriber's telephone number from a fixed relation to the layout of the telephone plant. Again, it would be hard to estimate how much inconvenience the public, without it, would have experienced through frequent changes in telephone numbers, but this would also have been large. Moreover, the concept of translation, if not the legal language of the patent itself, is embodied in every one of the great computing systems which were built during and since World War II."*

Some of the first work in applying probability theory to the handling of telephone traffic had been done by M. C. Rorty of AT&T as early as 1903. Before that time, generally, engineers had simply counted how many calls people made on the average and observed the maximum number of conversations seen simultaneously on the switchboards. From these empirical studies, tables and curves were developed to guide new installations.

Rorty's innovations roused great interest but also presented difficulties and shortcomings. Molina was able to remove them and to develop a mathematical expression, known for some time as the Molina Formula, which offered a sound basis for probability curves.

---

*Letter from Fry to R. I. Wilkinson, January 31, 1949.

Not until years later was it discovered that the French mathematician S. D. Poisson, a century or so before, had obtained the same mathematical expression, which now universally bears his name rather than Molina's. Whatever the name, however, it was Molina who produced it here in America for timely application early in this century.

Many other contributions have been made to the mathematical treatment of traffic, notably those of A. K. Erlang of Denmark, which became known to Bell engineers in 1918. And Molina, in his turn, made contributions in other fields than that of probability. He invented several widely used circuit arrangements, contributed to the design of transmission systems, and in later years published a theory of random sampling for general engineering use. He is also remembered for a special vitality and drive that greatly influenced the work of his associates. Following his retirement from Bell Laboratories in 1942, he at last "went to college," so to speak, and did so for more than 20 years—as a lecturer recognized as one of the foremost students of Laplace and a leading authority on classical mathematical probability.

Molina in his home library.

directly, and step by step, as dial pulses came over the line. The invention of translation by E. C. Molina of AT&T in 1906 freed the switching art from this limited kind of operation and led to mechanisms that could store and control the pulses in such a way as to make the whole process of interconnection more efficient and flexible. This development took some years and was interrupted by World War I, but starting in the 1920's the conversion of Bell System service from manual to dial operation went ahead rapidly. In the main, common control systems went into large metropolitan areas where the diversity of interconnection problems called for something more sophisticated than step-by-step equipment. Elsewhere step-by-step systems, which require less initial investment, have been widely used.

As conversion to dial operation proceeded, the development of better switching systems proceeded also. In particular, Bell engineers found the crossbar switch, originally conceived by R. J. Reynolds of Western Electric's Engineering Department and improved in Sweden, especially well adapted to common-control operation. In Sweden crossbar systems were operated for years in the step-by-step mode, but in America, in the 1930's and 1940's, Bell Laboratories development engineers pushed common-control ideas to the limit to create what were generally recognized—until the advent of electronic switching—as the most versatile and proficient machines for interconnection ever devised. The reader has already glimpsed some of the talents of these machines in long-distance switching; their companion systems have been equally proficient in local exchange and metropolitan area service.

PERSISTENT PROBLEMS

It should not be supposed, however, that switching technology has followed a smooth path. It has not. The essence of the switching engineer's complaint (as heard at Bell Laboratories anyway) is "Down with step-by-step!" A machine installed years ago, in a community of moderate size, in consideration of prudent investment practice and then foreseeable need, may present problems today. Cities have grown. New metropolitan areas have come into being. Networks once relatively simple are now remarkably complex, and the patterns and nature of communications traffic have changed. New services that are handled with comparative facility through crossbar and electronic systems are less readily provided where the switching is step-by-step.

True, common-control features have been added to step-by-step systems and other adjuncts have been improvised. And year by year, over the next 25 years, step-by-step switching will be phased out as rapidly as economic considerations can justify. But still through present air sounds the engineer's plaintive cry, "Stamp out step!"

The same problem applies, it may be added, elsewhere in the world, and to an even greater degree. In most countries step-by-step equipment is used more than any other; and intercity customer dialing, where it is available, also operates on step-by-step principles and requires varying numbers of digits, depending on where the call starts and where it is to go.

In the Bell System at the end of 1973, as noted earlier, nine per cent of all customer lines were served through electronic switching systems (which might be thought of as the "ultimate" form of common control systems). Another 50 per cent were served through crossbar systems, three per cent through an older form of common control system—the panel system—now rapidly being replaced, and 38 per cent by step-by-step equipment. All long-distance switching systems, as we have seen, are extraordinarily sophisticated and becoming even more so; for instance, electronic *translator* systems associated with crossbar long-distance switching machines have increased their capacity some 20 per cent. If present expectations are realized, by 1985 ESS machines will be serving about 50 per cent of the Bell System's customer lines.

As the heading for this chapter suggests, interconnectedness is an endless problem, especially because millions of new telephones must be added to the network each year. Growth must be taken care of as well as modernization; everything cannot be done at once; and come what may, old and new must always be made to work together. It should be said too that the merits of common-control switching have been debated through the years. The evidence of the present, however—the increasing complexity of social organization, the diversity of services that must course through switching systems, the permeation of switching by electronic devices and computer principles—indisputably indicates that this will be the direction of future progress. It also seems fair to say that while many people in many places have made brilliant contributions to the switching art, Bell Laboratories people have been in the front rank and time has demonstrated the soundness of their approach.

Finally, in switching as in transmission, dependable operation at reasonable cost demands quality and longevity in materials and components. Contacts must be perfect. Diodes must behave just right. Relay switches that have to operate hundreds of millions of times or more must do so without fail. Test equipment must swiftly and surely announce and locate troubles. It is almost impossible to overstate the demands on development and manufacture when, for example, 1000 or more operations are required to establish a single connection and in the total system trillions of components, all told, are involved. It was mentioned above that electronic switching "downtime" in 1973 came to about 13 minutes a year per central office, on the average. Sounds good, but it is not good enough; the objective is two hours in 40 years, which figures out to three minutes a year. Similarly, the normal criterion for electromagnetic relay performance is one failure in 40 years.

These requirements are mentioned simply as a reminder that much of the effort at Bell Laboratories underlying switching, as well as transmission, must go into the establishment of standards, the discovery and development of materials, and analysis of component and system performance that will insure systems not only sound in concept but durable and dependable in action. Further—and this again reflects the close present-day collaboration of Laboratories and telephone company people—Bell Laboratories is now developing control centers that will centralize the maintenance of groups of electronic and electromechanical switching offices in given areas. These centers are based on the results of studies and trials conducted jointly with the telephone companies. They are designed to provide continuous oversight over operations, head off potential troubles, automatically correct others, and bring expert skills promptly to bear wherever needed. Thus *development,* in the modern world of communications, relates not only to the system itself, but also to systems for operating the system.

Portable units that make up an electronic switching system designed by Bell Laboratories for small suburban or rural communities are trucked to Sun Valley, Nevada. At the site, the modules were erected on a prepared foundation in one day. Because they are pre-assembled and pre-tested at the factory, such offices are able to go into service quickly.

The small cylindrical object being lowered into a liquid-helium bath is a superconducting electromagnet. Its electrical resistance drops to zero at temperatures close to absolute zero. Bell Laboratories has conducted research on superconductivity since 1950.

ON THE RESEARCH SCENE

7

In December of 1972, twenty-five years after invention of the transistor at Bell Laboratories, the inventors, John Bardeen, Walter Brattain and William Shockley, were invited "to say a few words." With appropriate modesty they did so.

Bardeen recalled the importance of thorough study of semiconductor theory as it had developed in the 1920's and 1930's; and the importance, also, following the invention, of the "ingenious methods developed by many people for designing and controlling the distribution of the minute concentrations of impurities on which the properties (of transistors) depend."

Said Brattain, "The importance of an active solid-state circuit element was thoroughly recognized by anybody working in this area from about 1925 on, but . . . direct attempts to make such elements were futile, whereas the research work to try to understand what was really going on in the simplest semi-conductors, silicon and germanium, finally resulted in the breakthrough."

Shockley observed that the failures experienced turned out to be creative, for they led to the basic research that brought success. He added, "The managerial art of optimizing the interaction between pure and applied research is what makes Bell Laboratories so eminent a leader in innovation."

The three inventors, among them, thus made clear enough the need to dig deep, and also the need to take effective follow-up action as soon as discovery is made.

Years earlier, in a talk about research in physics, Mervin J. Kelly, then president of Bell Laboratories, asserted that the application of new knowledge from research in physics, chemistry and mathematics had been "the central element in the Laboratories' large contributions of the past 40 years to communications technology."[*] Kelly spoke also of then current studies of surface states and energy levels in numerous solid materials—studies which, as it has turned out, led to the integrated circuits, solid-state lasers and other remarkable components essential to systems now in use or in various stages of development.

---

[*]"The Work and Environment of the Physicist," *Physics Today*, Vol. 10, No. 4 (April 1957).

A year or so later F. R. Kappel, then president of AT&T, gave his view of research as a business manager. The Bell System, he said, had to keep acquiring new knowledge and this called for a special brand of brains. Then he commented, "You have to have an objective but you also have to give the brains full freedom. Maybe those two things will strike you as mutually exclusive. That has not been our experience. We have the broad objective of improving electrical communication. This is a perfectly clear goal. At the same time, it gives the research scientist full scope for the exercise of his creative power. If you question this, I suggest you ask our scientists."*

To a limited extent the present writer has done this. The answers generally bear Mr. Kappel out.

A young physicist, for instance, remarked that he feels a greater freedom at Bell Laboratories than he experienced at the university, for the reason that he does not have to carry a teaching schedule.

A mathematician who left a university teaching job to join the fledgling Bell Laboratories computing research group in the 1950's replied: "Things have developed here because individual people at the working level have had ideas and have pursued them.

"Interested specialists have wanted to make their contribution. Management approval is a subsequent step. For many years in the research department the policy all the way up the line was clearly one of saying: 'We are convinced that computers are going to have a major role in the future; let's be part of the leading edge here. Let's encourage people to work in this field, but let's not assign somebody to do this and somebody to do that.' "

And another veteran of many years in Bell Laboratories research: "Research ideas occur to one person at a time; innovations are not made by teams.

Sometimes you get two people at a blackboard, or three people working on a project. Sometimes, by talking to each other every day and kicking things around, they get an idea and it will be impossible to say who had the idea first. But generally your quantum jumps are made by one person.

"I don't mean to say that people all make quantum jumps every day. But this is what research is about; it is to have people who are not bound by production jobs, service jobs or current technology jobs, but who are asking themselves (or at least in the ideal state they are asking themselves) all the time, what are the real problems going to be in five, ten, fifteen years? What do we really want to do and how are we going to do it? And then, in order to have some notion of how we are going to do it, we need to understand the problems pretty deeply. But the basic thing research people always have to keep before their eyes is what will need to be done, what can we do, several years down the pike."

Dr. Sidney Millman, for some years executive director of research in physics, was emphatic about the freedom accorded scientists in that area. To illustrate, he recalled an occasion when Ali Javan, a co-inventor of the first continuously operating gas laser, had said how pleased he was that no one had questioned him about his having ordered equipment for a line of work which, on reconsideration, he had decided not to pursue.

Millman recalled also, from his own experience, that while he had been invited from time to time by development engineers to advise them as a consultant, he was never obliged to do so. The decision was always his.

The late Estill I. Green, an executive vice president of Bell Laboratories in the 1950's, thought it essential that research people be "in the stream of problems," but vastly important also that they be free from what he called "the invasions and crises of the development turmoil." And in the writings and

---

*"Business Needs Basic Research," Talk by F. R. Kappel before The Economic Club of New York, January 21, 1958.

pronouncements of Bell Laboratories administrators through the years, one finds repeatedly expressed the understanding that scientists at work there must be known and respected as free citizens of the scientific community.

Varying employment arrangements also contribute to research freedom and vitality at Bell Laboratories. Some staff members hold joint appointments at the Laboratories and at a university. Others hold limited-term appointments and may move on after a year or two. Some appointees may have stipends from other institutions for work at the Laboratories. Many staff members, in turn, with the cooperation of the management, take time for advanced or refresher study at universities.

At Bell Laboratories as elsewhere, the presence of talent tends to attract talent. William Shockley, for instance, has said that he was first drawn there

In the Bell Laboratories auditorium at West Street, New York City, in 1927, AT&T president W. S. Gifford watches and talks to Herbert Hoover during the first public demonstration of intercity television. H. E. Ives, who directed the development for Bell Laboratories, stands at right. The other observers, from left, are E. P. Clifford, vice president, H. D. Arnold, director of research, E. B. Craft, vice president and F. B. Jewett, president, all of Bell Laboratories.

because he wanted to work with C. J. Davisson, the first member of the staff to have been awarded a Nobel prize (page 97). Another Nobel laureate, Professor Eugene Wigner of Princeton University, commented recently that while it was his "impression" that Bell Laboratories is the best industrial research laboratory in the country, this has not been his principal reason for recommending to some of his students that they apply for appointments. Rather, he said, "It is that I know several excellent physicists and helpful and astute collaborators there who maintain a friendly and stimulating atmosphere that I feel will be beneficial to new members of the group."

Said Professor Wigner also, "The leadership is competent and not very interfering. They know that making an invention is not like digging up the garden —it is intuitive and comes to you. So if somebody wants to go on a binge they let him do it; one cannot say that it may be unrelated. After all, it was not wholly clear that semiconductor study would come to something."

A WIDE, WIDE WORLD

Obviously, research toward "the broad objective of improving electrical communication," as Kappel put it, must cover considerable ground. When a young staff member remarks, "This organization provides opportunity for an incredible variety of work," the comment applies within the research area as well as to Bell Laboratories as a whole.

In budget terms, however, the research department represents a relatively small part—about 12 per cent—of Bell Laboratories' total technical effort. And even this percentage is somewhat misleading, for it suggests that all Laboratories research is equally "fundamental" in nature, and that is not the case. Three-quarters or more of the effort in physics is regarded as fundamental and the proportion of fundamental work in mathematics and statistics, and in the electronics research area, may also approach that. On the other hand, much research department activity relating to radio, guided waves, computing science, chemistry and materials science is project-oriented even though it is not scheduled or programmed in the same sense as are specific engineering developments.

Such gradations should not surprise, for there must be, after all, several stages of work between the search for knowledge and its discovery and use. Indeed, a main reason why the semiconductor revolution moved as fast as it did in the 1950's was the many-

sided exploratory development program at Bell Laboratories that followed on the heels of invention of the transistor. It was this, as we have seen, that produced the pure crystals, the techniques for impurity diffusion, oxide masking, thermo-compression bonding, epitaxial growth and other advances on which modern solid-state and integrated-circuit technology have been built.

BENEFITS FROM RESEARCH

The late Julius P. Molnar, executive vice president of Bell Laboratories at the time of his death in 1973, summarized four values of research.

"There is first," he said, "the strictly scientific part, the findings, analyses and generalizations. They bring us respect from the outside, especially from the academic community. More importantly, they provide the scientific foundations for subsequent applications-oriented work." Examples noted elsewhere in this book include information theory, the mathematics underlying wave filters, understanding of thermal noise and single-sideband transmission, the principle of common control in switching, negative feedback, findings in acoustics and optics, and solid-state physics generally.

Another, and relatively new, concept that Molnar referred to as of possible comparable significance is that of multidimensional scaling. This is a method of managing information which, thanks to the computer, makes it possible to discern correlations previously beyond reach by reason of their being so embedded in complex, profuse data. Now, new comparisons may be made—as among, perhaps, apples and oranges. The first ideas in multidimensional scaling were advanced elsewhere, but it is generally considered that work at Bell Laboratories has given the subject decisive impetus.

The second value Molnar named was the discovery and refinement of understanding of phenomena and materials that can be put to good use. This value

continued on page 99

Clinton J. Davisson

Bell Laboratories' First Nobel Prize Winner

C. J. Davisson came to the research section of the Engineering Department of Western Electric in 1917, on leave from the Carnegie Institute of Technology. He intended to stay only during the war period, to help in the development of vacuum tubes for military communications. But he remained with the engineering organization, later to become Bell Laboratories, nearly 30 years. In 1927, in a classic experiment at the Laboratories, he bombarded a crystal of nickel with a stream of electrons and the electrons were diffracted (dispersed) in waves corresponding to the momentum of the electrons. For this conclusive demonstration of the wave nature of matter, Davisson in 1937 shared the Nobel Prize in Physics with G. P. Thomson of England, who had achieved a similar result using different techniques.

Several points may be of interest.

First, Davisson was an analytical scientist working on fundamental problems of the physics of vacuum tubes. Harold D. Arnold, then the director of research (see p. 21), encouraged him to develop a pattern of work of his own choosing.

Second, the work that won the Nobel Prize for Davisson grew out of studies of immense importance to the communications art. Improvements in vacuum tubes—longer life, economy, capabilities —depended on complete understanding of extremely complex phenomena. In particular, as the structures and circuits became more complicated, major problems developed that could only be controlled if the reasons for them were fully understood. It was in the course of research on "secondary emission" of electrons in thermionic tubes that Davisson came on patterns of emission from crystals of nickel that made him curious and led him to his discovery.

Third, subsequent to Davisson's achievement, L. H. Germer, who had worked with him during his researches, devised methods for using electron diffraction to study the crystalline structure of surface films. Thus, from Davisson's work came a valuable new means to aid analysis of ongoing problems. The study of surfaces was already an important phase of electronics research and has become even more so with the development of semiconductor technology.

Davisson went on to study problems in electron optics and the physics of crystals, and he exerted great influence as a consultant and as adviser to younger men who were introduced to Bell Laboratories through association with him.

A 1951 memoir on Davisson by M. J. Kelly, published soon after Kelly became president of Bell Laboratories, throws light both on Davisson's qualities and on the research policy of Bell Labs.

"He established a pattern of fundamental research," Kelly wrote, "that has continued and enlarged in scope as our laboratories have evolved and reached maturity. Across the forefronts of physics, mathematics and chemistry, which are basic to communications technology, we now have many scientists whose programs are directed, as was Davisson's, only at expanding fundamental knowledge, and who do not divert their energies even to the fundamental development phases . . . It is a tribute to Davisson's overpowering interest in science . . . that during the pioneering and rapid-expansion years of our laboratories he gave almost undivided attention to the scientific aspects of our work."*

*M. J. Kelly, "Dr. C. J. Davisson," *Bell System Technical Journal,* Vol. XXX, No. 4 (October, 1951), pp. 779-785.

On December 10, 1937, King Gustaf of Sweden presented a Nobel Prize in Physics to Davisson and G. P. Thomson of Great Britain for discovery of the wave nature of matter.

In 1927, Davisson (right) and his associate, Lester H. Germer, with the tube they used in their classic experiments.

relates not only to the transistor as an obvious example but to various forms of lasers, the behavior of radio waves, the millimeter waveguide system, and the properties of crystals, plastics, gases, and magnetic, superconducting, and insulating materials.

"A third benefit," Molnar said, "is the window our research activity gives us to the outside scientific world. As active participants and contributors in the research community, we get advance notice of what is happening elsewhere and are in a good position to evaluate the discoveries of others." It takes only a moment's thought to appreciate the importance of this: if Bell System service is to benefit from scientific discovery wherever it may be, the Bell System must have people who are competent to understand it and appraise its potential.

"The fourth and last benefit," Molnar said, "is more subtle. By digging deeply into fundamental questions, by reexamining old ideas too long accepted without question, and by continuing to show that the rational, scientific approach does work, our research people demonstrate what the human mind can achieve. In so doing they set the tone for all our work at Bell Laboratories. They lend encouragement and give confidence to the rest of the Laboratories organization for taking similar approaches to the less scientific and more technological problems that are encountered in carrying out the other parts of our mission."

This thought of research setting the tone for all of Bell Laboratories' work is not a suggestion that research is a cut above development in the R&D pecking order.* It means rather that research should provide the sure knowledge that first-rate development people have a right to expect and know they can depend on. Also, advancing the frontiers of knowledge opens up horizons that make development exciting. One may hear, among the managers of development at the Laboratories, varying opinions as to the effectiveness of this or that particular line of research, but never the view that basic research is something that the Laboratories could get along without.

Three other points often noted about the research activity seem usefully to supplement those discussed by Molnar.

*See Dr. Fisk's remarks quoted on page 6.

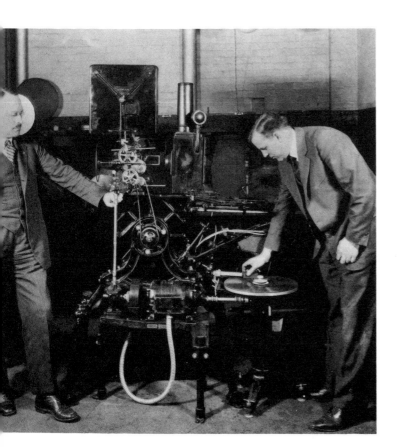

Engineers H. M. Stoller (left) and A. S. Pfannstiehl working on the Bell Laboratories "talking movie machine" that added sound to film. The machine helped launch the "talking picture" era with the Broadway premier of Warner-Vitaphone's "The Jazz Singer," starring Al Jolson, in 1927. Earlier systems had provided music backgrounds but no speech.

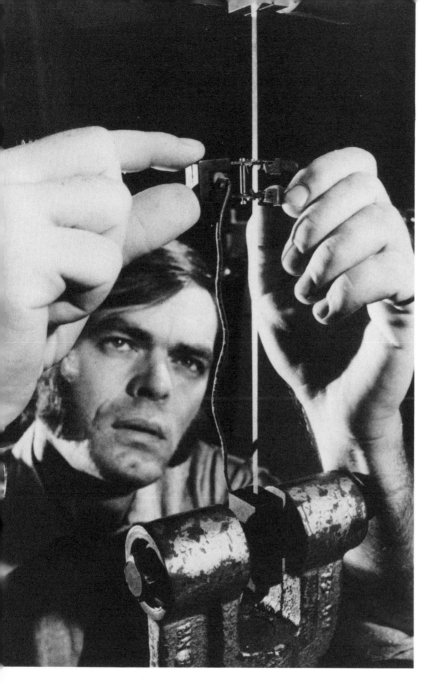

Springier springs for Bell System communications equipment is the promise of a new family of copper alloys developed at Bell Laboratories in 1974. A research metallurgist is shown preparing a sample of the new alloy for test on a machine that pulls the sample apart and records the stress and strain.

One is that there is some movement into development of brilliant researchers who become interested in specific development problems. Second, not a few research people become good administrators. All but the first of the five Bell Laboratories presidents, in fact, and many other officers as well, started in research. The first one, F. B. Jewett, came to the AT&T Engineering Department in 1904 with a doctorate in physics from the University of Chicago. Managers of industrial laboratories have to have technical as well as administrative competence, and it is doubtless something other than chance that has brought so many research people to positions of leadership.

The third point relates to the consulting function referred to by Dr. Millman. It is extremely valuable to have experts around; and to get their advice, it is not necessary to draw them into what Green called "the development turmoil." Discussion can be informed, occasional and enjoyable. Witness this comment from an engineer working on computer programs to be used in telephone company operations. "It has often been said," he remarked, "that if you need to find out something at Bell Laboratories, the guy who wrote the book is right down the hall. I've found this to be in general true. Not only so— they are willing to sit down with you and discuss your problem and get you headed in the right direction."

The consulting role, it should be added, extends in some instances not only to other departments of Bell Laboratories but throughout the whole Bell System. Chemists and other specialists in materials science, particularly, are often needed to help solve technical problems in the telephone companies. This is not surprising when it is recalled that telephone calls depend on countless metal contacts in atmospheres that contain corrosive elements, and that transmission structures are subject to every conceivable variation in soil and climate. In another research area, that of computing science, consulting opportunities are also increasing as computer techniques are applied to more and more operational problems.

CONTINUITY WITH RENEWAL

Naturally enough, Bell Laboratories research through the years has changed its emphasis as older problems have been resolved and new ones presented themselves. Research in transmission, for example, was marked in earlier years by analysis of the problem of fading speech currents, study of vacuum-tube problems and structures, the search for magnetic alloys, measurement of radio-wave propagation, and the definition and refinement of fundamental transmission principles. Now work on transmission has moved into new fields. One of them is the study of rainfall, which affects millimeter radio waves, and how to lay out radio systems using such waves in a manner that will assure continuous good communications notwithstanding the rain. Transmission research has also been closely concerned with the refinement of knowledge bearing on waveguide systems. A third vital concern is research into the structure of optical systems of transmission. Still another phase of study has centered on new methods of processing digital pulses; a few words about this will help to make an important point.

Chapter 3 outlined how carrier systems have provided more and more communication circuits at low costs per mile. These systems require at their terminals, among other things, so-called "channel banks" that stack circuits at different frequencies side by side. One of the big goals in transmission today is to get the cost of these down, and it now looks as though new digital techniques, using large-scale integrated circuits, will help a lot in this respect—even in the case of channel banks that produce not digital but analog (wavelike) circuits. Similar new techniques have led to more reliable and economical equipment for Touch-Tone® signaling and to a four-to-one reduction in the transmission capacity needed for Picturephone® service.

This is a good example of what has been called the *continuity with renewal* characteristic of Bell Laboratories research—a continuous effort refreshed and renewed as accumulating insights are applied to new problems in new ways. Also, the very nature of the Bell System, with its vast and diverse physical plant, its steady growth, and the endless opportunities it offers for orderly improvement, tends to favor a continuous program of research. Such a program can be large enough to get results but still modest in terms of its cost, which comes to about twenty cents out of every hundred dollars of Bell System revenue.

Continuity with renewal: the thought is well illustrated also by the course of acoustic and visual research. To the knowledge of speech and hearing, for example, gained through the years by Harvey Fletcher and his associates (see page 117), recent work has added much more. Computer-aided studies have revealed, for instance, how the human vocal tract works and how the human auditory system processes signals. Such research has recently led to systems (still experimental) that enable computers to synthesize speech from written text; the speech is still somewhat monotonous but acceptable for some purposes. Another system uses digital techniques for computer synthesis of stored speech sounds, so that messages can be produced as needed. Thus a worker on a detailed technical job can be guided by instructions heard through earphones, instead of having to keep looking at a book. Such instructions, or informational announcements, as the case may be, can be quickly changed as needed without the necessity to make new recordings. Still another new system enables a computer to recognize voices stored in its memory; and so we have the possibility (in a "checkless" society?) that a person who wishes to be identified over the telephone may simply call in, speak a few words, be recognized, and proceed with his or her business.

CONTINUITY IN VISUAL RESEARCH

Work in visual communication has also had a long history at Bell Laboratories. Years of research before World War II produced knowledge of how and when it is that people see a flicker of light as continuous, and how the eye requires that in a color image containing blue, red and green only the green need be sharply focused. Later study showed that the eye could not absorb all the information a television channel could convey; this stimulated successive, and successful, efforts to take advantage of the characteristic properties of pictures themselves in order to reduce the bandwidth required to transmit them. All such work has strongly influenced the course of television and other picture transmission. And more recently, visual research has reached toward the possibilities for three-dimensional transmission, toward understanding of how human beings recognize what they see and into the very process of visual learning.

The spectrum of research at Bell Laboratories is rather too broad to allow touching on all of it here even in summary fashion. Also, a good many research results have been noted along the way in other chapters and in the brief notes about some of the people who have played significant roles. We shall confine the rest of this chapter, therefore, to two areas—materials science and computers. In both, the theme of continuity with renewal will also be apparent.

MATERIALS SCIENCE

Materials science at Bell Laboratories, intensified in the past quarter-century or more by successes realized from the study of "the secret motions of things" (Francis Bacon's phrase) ranges all the way from basic research to engineering. Dr. Baker, who was in charge of research before he became the Laboratories' president, takes the view that the study of materials is one of the compelling scientific movements of the mid-20th century. He also argues that this came about largely because of the

Bell System's need to meet a simultaneous set of demands under complex conditions of commerce and use. What demands? Well, essentially, physical systems using components in huge quantity had to be made to last, notwithstanding incessant precise and exacting operation. Even that simple unit, a wire, had to perform both structurally and electrically in all kinds of environments. It was, Baker says, "the terrible set of expectations" the Bell System had for materials "that drove us to become the cradle of solid-state science and engineering."

Baker says further, "The universities don't have to face the same kind of problem. They can choose one atom to study, not a box of atoms, a thing that contains 10^{23} atoms per cubic centimeter. And they are in general right. For their purpose it is wise to keep everything as simple as possible. But our world did not permit that. We have had to deal with mechanical properties, electrical properties, economic and environmental properties, magnetic properties— all at once. And that is really the essence of modern materials science and engineering."

Bruce Hannay, now vice president in charge of research and previously head of the materials research division, observes that materials science is in fact a complex of interdisciplinary effort involving chemists, metallurgists, physicists, mechanical engineers, ceramists and others. A significant part of their work goes toward synthesizing materials. To do this, Hannay says, "ideally one would start out with a list of all the desirable macroscopic properties, such as electrical conductivity, light absorption, modulus, and so forth, and then use fundamental principles to put together the right atoms in the right structure. Success lies in being smart enough to decide which relationships are important and which are not, and thus to narrow the search."

Today, Hannay and Baker agree, Bell Laboratories scientists are close to the point where they can devise a material to meet a requirement. "The possibility that you could do that with polymers was one of the

continued on page 105

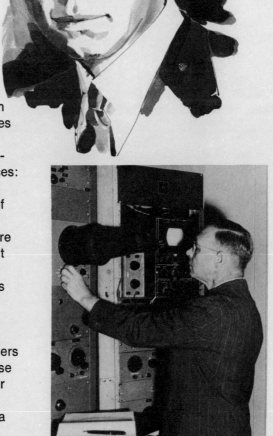
John B. Johnson

Johnson Noise

Twenty-five years ago, answering a request for information about himself, John Bertrand Johnson wrote ten short lines in longhand. The sixth line said, "Cleared up fundamental sources of circuit noise in 1925-30."

Noise, the ubiquitous, unwanted, insistent, unwelcome gate-crasher of electrical communication circuits, has several sources: the closing of a switch, the crackle emanating from distant thunder, the voltage induced from a nearby circuit, the heat of the sun, radiation from galaxies light-years away—and the physical nature of the circuit itself. In all electrical circuits there is some resistance, some heat, and, perforce, a certain amount of noise arising from random thermal fluctuations. This noise, present at every point where there is resistance, is sometimes called thermal noise, sometimes white noise, and sometimes Johnson noise by reason of Johnson's contributions to the understanding of its nature.

More specifically, Johnson's analysis of vacuum-tube amplifiers led him to demonstrate the existence of thermal and other noise effects predicted years before by the German scientist Walther Schottky, and made it possible to define the limits to which communication signals could be amplified usefully. This was a fundamental contribution to electronics. The *Johnson effect* concept derived from these studies was universally applied in the vacuum-tube amplifier field, and the knowledge supporting it has been translated into terms applicable to solid-state amplifiers after the transistor was invented.

Earlier in his career, J. B. Johnson also developed the first sealed cathode-ray oscillograph tube; or, to quote his own long-hand note about himself once more, he "made C. R. oscillograph a common laboratory tool in 1922."

Johnson, designer of the first commercial cathode-ray tube, adjusts a cathode-ray oscillograph, which he developed into a standard tool for engineering and scientific laboratories.

Early acoustics research at Bell Laboratories indicated the need for an anechoic chamber, a "free-space" room devoid of echoes and reverberations. Here, a Bell Laboratories scientist performs an acoustic experiment in the chamber at Murray Hill, N.J. Reflection-free sound conditions are vital for certain studies of speech and hearing, and for testing equipment that produces and receives sound.

things that pushed us down the road of intensive polymer study," says Baker, and Hannay adds, "In this field we are now in a position to tailor-make properties."

In metals, progress has been slower. "Empirically," Baker points out, "one can cover a lot of needs by making a lot of alloys. But you are not quite sure what is doing what. However, we now have knowledge of dislocations in crystals that answers age-old questions. We know why crystals grow as they do and the origin of processes we must control. And now that we know what the metal is depending on—partly on composition, partly on crystal structure perfection, partly on dislocations—I think (and I must say this cautiously) I think we can begin to make designs for a particular property in a metal's atomic base."

The importance of mastery of materials in the Bell System can hardly be overemphasized. If practical optical communications systems are to be realized, for instance, it may well be by reason (among other things) of glass fibers of a purity and clarity never before obtained;* by reason also of new and better materials for lasers and other system components; or even by reason of diodes that emit invisible beams of infrared light through the open atmosphere. To the layman, some of the substances under study for such purposes are exotic to say the least. For instance, the first continuous solid-state laser that could operate at room temperature used calcium tungstate doped with neodymium. Another employed yttrium aluminum garnet, likewise doped with neodymium. Two of the various compounds used experimentally to modulate the light beam have been lithium tantalate and barium strontium niobate. Others for other purposes include lithium niobate and barium sodium niobate, tellurium oxide, and various iodine compounds.

*Corning Glass Company, it should be pointed out, has made striking contributions here. As an indication of the clarity that has been achieved, if ocean water were equally clear, the ocean floor anywhere in the world could be seen from the surface.

PROCESSES

Materials science is largely concerned with processes. Such concern led years ago to a process for producing synthetic quartz crystal—material that has become standard for precision filters and frequency controls. It led to the "zone melting" process that produced ultrapure semiconductor crystals and to the various other processes mentioned on page 73 that have been basic to transistor and integrated-circuit technology. More recently, materials scientists have developed "ion implantation" techniques for introducing minute amounts of impurities in crystals—literally ion by ion. They have devised a method of processing iron oxide films for integrated circuits that will greatly reduce the time needed to make circuit patterns. In the case of so-called "hybrid" integrated circuits, which combine semiconductor chips with other circuit elements on thin films, they have been able to halve the number of steps needed to create the thin-film structure. Other new processes have greatly facilitated the manufacture of many plastic components and have achieved unprecedented uniformity and performance in ceramic bodies.

Materials scientists are also studying how materials function in thin films; the objective is to make them more reliable. They are growing crystals for semiconductor lasers in successive layers, with each layer having a different composition. They have grown crystals of lithium tantalate that are now being used as electrical filters for data transmission—filters smaller and simpler than quartz crystals, and also able to operate over a wider band of frequencies. Subjecting various materials to ultrahigh pressure, they are learning how their properties may change under different conditions. They have produced tungsten-rubidium films that at certain temperatures are harder than any known metal, and glassy alloys having twice the tensile strength of high-carbon spring steel.

Not all materials science at Bell Laboratories deals with exotic substances with outlandish names. Far

Several hundred gas and solid-state lasers have been discovered at Bell Laboratories. One of them, shown above, was the first gas laser to generate a continuous beam of visible light (1962). In addition to applications in communications, lasers have been used by Western Electric to make diamond wire dies, to spot-weld and to aid in manufacture of electronic circuits.

from it. There is intense concern also with plain hardware like wire, cable, relay springs and other items that have long been in daily use. Thus, for example, materials research finds that high-energy electron radiation will toughen wire insulation. New chemical controls reduce or prevent flammability, and antioxidant combinations extend the life of cable sheathing. Air control systems are specified to protect equipment against corrosion, methods are developed to detect gaseous pollutants, and emission controls are applied to telephone company heating plants and emergency power engines.

MAGNETIC BUBBLES

One other example in the field of materials science —in association with physics—shows strikingly the interdisciplinary character of work at Bell Laboratories. This is the development of what have come to be called magnetic bubbles.

The story began many years ago with fundamental physical studies of the behavior of materials in magnetic fields. Why, among other things, did a material break up its magnetic content when magnetized? The physicists found that in doing this it minimized its energy, and that there were walls or boundaries within which, in separate domains, energy would point in different directions. Studying these domains, with the help of chemists who devised ways to reveal them, they came at length to the study of garnets, which showed unusual properties first investigated in Holland and France.

"These insulating magnets (the garnets)," Baker explains, "had the most minute and delicate domains and many of them minimized their energy in tiny circles. Now, Bill Shockley had the idea that you could move these domains or bubbles around and he and Andy Bobeck showed this could be done. However, the bubbles didn't move very fast. But then Van Uitert, a chemist, thought there might be ways to change the energy of the crystals compositionally so that they would move fast. By a remarkable series of reasonings (not so far from the point that you can almost make materials on the basis of property) he synthesized what we call supergarnets; and these are the basis of modern bubble memories now being tried out in an experimental switching system."

What is the significance of the magnetic bubble? "It represents," says Baker, "a remarkable combination of memory and logic—something not easy to come by. The logic comes from whether the bubble

continued on page 110

Karl G. Jansky

The Father of Radio Astronomy

A young father he was, too—for Karl Jansky was only 22 when he started work at Bell Laboratories to record and measure radio static. This was in 1928. Overseas radiotelephone service had started only a year or so earlier and knowing more about noise was important. Four years later, in 1932, Jansky published a paper in which he classified three kinds of static: that from local thunderstorms, that from distant thunderstorms, and "a steady hiss static, the origin of which is not known."

Let Dr. Harald Friis, in whose group Jansky was working, continue the story. "The hiss-type static, or hiss noise, fascinated Karl," Friis wrote years later. "Having collected thousands of records, he discussed the data with his colleague A. M. Skellet, who was familiar with astronomy. The conclusion was that the hiss noise came from the Milky Way."* This conclusion, reported by Jansky in papers published in 1933, was supported by the fact that the noise, which sounded like the fluctuating "thermal" noise in electrical circuits, was strongest when Jansky pointed the antenna he was using at the Milky Way's center.

This discovery was one of the epochal events in the history of science. For centuries astronomers had studied the heavens using optical techniques alone. Now, for the first time, the mysteries of heavenly bodies, and of space itself, were manifesting themselves through the radio spectrum as well.

Yet strangely, scientists were slow to grasp the meaning of this revelation. Jansky himself, continuing at Bell Laboratories,

*"Karl Jansky: His Career at Bell Telephone Laboratories," *Science,* Vol. 149, No. 3686 (August 20, 1965), p. 841.

expanded his work to study how transatlantic radio waves arrived at receiver stations; he became, in fact, an expert in selecting favorable receiver sites. But as Dr. Friis also recalls, five years after Jansky had reported his findings and conclusions, the term "radio astronomy" still did not exist and no word of encouragement to continue work on "star noise," as he later called it, had come from scientists or astronomers.

In 1941, however, studies by Grote Reber, an enthusiastic radio amateur, confirmed Jansky's work; and after World War II radio astronomy started in earnest. Already its results have been profound. Since radio waves can penetrate the dust of space and planetary clouds that may limit optical observations, the new science has greatly increased understanding of solar phenomena and the physical processes that occur in interstellar space. Using huge radio telescopes, ultrasensitive amplifiers, and computers, radio astronomers have organized new knowledge transmitted from the sun, from our galaxy, and from nebulae beyond. The most dramatic discovery has been that of the existence of quasars, those "quasi-stellar" bodies that generate continuous power at many frequencies and constitute sources of energy never guessed at before.

Karl Jansky, always frail in health, died in 1950, before he could see the full significance of his discovery. An important aspect of his work, be it added, lies directly within the field of communications and has been powerfully demonstrated by other Bell Laboratories scientists within the last few years.

Using advanced techniques of millimeter-wave spectroscopy, which is in effect a form of radio astronomy, they have discovered and studied "more molecules in outer space," to quote President W. O. Baker of Bell Laboratories, "than have been discovered in all the history of astronomy before." This knowledge, Dr. Baker says, has been invaluable in conjunction with efforts to exploit the bountiful spectrum of millimeter waves for radio communications.

"We have adopted the knowledge and challenge of radio astronomy," he comments, "to help establish our competence with millimeter waves. Today we can generate and control these waves economically—and can do so because we had this theoretical/practical testing system in space. If we had not had such insights from outer space, with the excitement and stimulus they provided . . . well, nobody ever imagined millimeter-wave radio could be made practical, nobody ever thought those waves

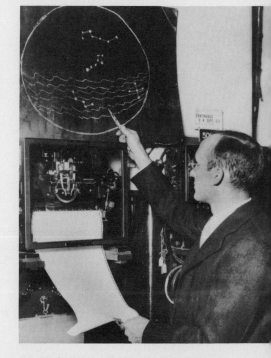

Jansky indicates the spot in the heavens from which radio noises from space were first heard.

could be used outdoors."

Further, Baker sees the opportunity to observe the behavior of molecules in space as affording what he calls "a new test tube for science. In these vast spatial reactors, molecular collisions are occurring orders of magnitude slower than they have ever been observed on earth—they are meters apart. So you have a model, magic situation where pair collisions take long times, you can observe the individual orientation of the molecules in space; and these are just the things we want to know in studying the stability of the hardware of the Bell System, in studying ways to make new components, in studying the interaction of charges and molecules in the electronics and circuitry of the System. So here is a whole new game."

A whole new game some 40 or more years after Karl Jansky's discovery; the frail young man's legacy to Bell Laboratories, to science, and to the world was large indeed.

Jansky with the rotatable antenna he used in studies of atmospheric noises that interfered with overseas radio telephone service. Among the noises, in 1933, he discovered a mysterious one coming from the center of the Milky Way. His discovery led to the new science of radio astronomy.

is there or not, the memory from the magnetic field that can be sensed if it is. Of course we have the vital question of producing enough of the stuff cheaply enough but I wouldn't say that that cannot be done. With the bubble's great advantage in compactness and speed—you can store millions of bits of information in a square inch of garnet crystal and move them in millionths of a second—it may win a real place for itself, although of course it will have to do so in competition with other devices."

Interestingly enough, magnetic bubbles were hardly out of the basic research area and into experimental development when a potential competitor did appear. People working with semiconductors thought, "Bubbles can be useful because they can be precisely manipulated. Can't we manipulate energies in semiconductors too?"

Two men, Willard S. Boyle and George E. Smith, "started batting ideas around," in Smith's words, "and invented *charge-coupled devices* in an hour. Yes, it was unusual—like a light bulb going on."

Charge-coupled devices, or CCD's, manipulate small packets of electrical charge in a slice of silicon or other suitable material. They can perform imaging, logic and memory functions, have already been tried experimentally in video transmission, and may come to wide use.

Now for computers:

COMPUTING SCIENCE AND COMPUTERS IN RESEARCH

There is a reason for the seemingly redundant heading above. The first two words relate to Bell Laboratories' part in developing the hardware of general-purpose computers and the concepts, operating systems and computer languages usually referred to as software. The rest of the heading takes note of what everyone knows; i.e., that most research today—like development and, to an increasing extent, the management of operations—uses and depends on computers.

More specifically, the heading suggests that some of the most advanced research at the Laboratories in recent years has attended the expansion of computer functions, yielding insights attainable only by reason of skillful and versatile use of the computer's power. Perhaps the distinction made in that long sentence is unnecessary. Perhaps a computer program that enables the machine to recognize human voices, or make differential equations visible in the motion of a satellite, is no more and no less a program than any other. However, we can leave that to the reader's taste.

In any case, Bell Laboratories' early contributions to digital computers—both hardware and software—quite evidently grew from the fact that telephone switching systems used digital logic and electrical relays, which are binary "on" or "off" devices, to make connections. Importantly also, in the late 1930's principles of logical design proposed by Claude E. Shannon (who later created information theory) were first applied to the design of relay circuits. These principles, together with two basic logic circuits patented by the Laboratories in the early 1940's, still underlie digital computer technology.

Also in the late 1930's, George R. Stibitz, another Bell Laboratories mathematician, designed a machine that used telephone switches and relays to perform rapid calculations in binary form. This Complex Number Calculator, as Stibitz called it, was in fact the first electrically operated digital computer in the United States. Locked in a closet, it could be reached only through three separately located teletypewriters; and with these terminals it constituted the first computing system with remote, multiple access. Late in 1940, Stibitz took one of his teletypewriters to a meeting of the American Mathematical Society in Hanover, New Hampshire, had it connected to the calculator in New York, and invited his confreres to type in problems. The machine sent the answers back briskly in minutes.

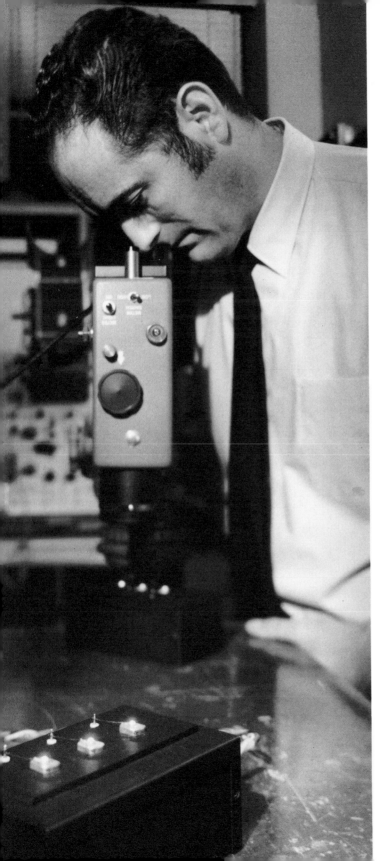

Bell Laboratories has developed new solid-state lamps called light-emitting diodes (LED's). LED's are far more durable and consume much less power than conventional tungsten lamps. They are being introduced as signal lamps and number indicators in communication equipment such as key telephone sets, data sets and operators' consoles.

During the war Stibitz and others at Bell Laboratories produced several relay-operated digital machines for military purposes. War needs and postwar defense programs also led the Laboratories, at government request, to develop various analog computers for control of antiaircraft guns and missiles, as noted in Chapter 10. And throughout these same years university scientists were also making basic contributions to computer development, in the course of which John Von Neumann of the Institute for Advanced Study at Princeton established the principle of the stored program; i.e., internal storage of instructions the machine itself can alter on command.

"These were the beginnings of modern computing," wrote Edward E. David, Jr., then executive director of communications system research at Bell Laboratories and later Science Adviser to the President.* "The first commercial stored-program computers became available in the early 1950's. It was commonly said that a general-purpose computer could do anything for anyone—it was simply a matter of programming. The complexities thus concealed were legion. This prompted R. W. Hamming of Bell Laboratories to say that a large computing machine without a reservoir of utility programs and language translators is about as useful to a researcher, or for that matter to any user, as a battleship without a crew is to a weekend sailing buff.

"From this realization," David continued, "came the concept of the hardware-software machine—a machine whose electronics are supplemented by

*E. E. David, "The Role of Research," *Bell Laboratories Record* (January, 1969), pp. 2-10.

111

stored programs which make it accessible and useful to a wide variety of users. Hamming and his colleagues created the first machine of this kind, drawing on other industrial and academic resources. These hardware-software systems were based on the IBM 650 and 704 computers, and it is from this work that today's time-shared, multiprogrammed, high 'through-put' systems come. The thinking behind such systems has given computing the scope to invade all fields of learning and enterprise and we are still pursuing this goal."

It was the transistor, as is generally known, that really

A Bell Laboratories scientist types English text into a computer, part of an experimental system that can convert printed text into synthetic speech. The oscilloscope screen (at right) displays the movement of the throat, face, tongue and lips with each changing sound in the computer's "voice." Such a system might someday retrieve computer-stored information and recite it in response to queries made over the telephone, either by voice or teletypewriter.

set the course of computer hardware technology. Less well known is the fact that in the early 1950's Bell Laboratories designed and built the first general-purpose transistor computer. This was used by the Air Force. The techniques applied in developing this machine, as well as one or two others for military projects, have been widely used in the computer industry. Since then, however, on the principle that the business of the Bell System is communications and not the production of computers for general use, Bell Laboratories' main contributions to the world of general-purpose machines have been software techniques and concepts designed to make them more useful in Bell System research, development and operations. Also, of course, Laboratories people have devised systems to promote the usefulness and ease of computer communications. Paralleling this has been the massive undertaking to create electronic switching systems, which are in fact a complex of ultrareliable, special-purpose, stored-program digital machines (see page 77).

STEPS IN COMPUTING SCIENCE

Writing about innovations in software must contend with the fact that they tend to wrap themselves in mists of computer jargon. Nevertheless it is possible to indicate some Bell Laboratories' work in the field in fairly plain terms.

For instance, most intermediate "assembler" computer programs, which translate the programs written by human beings into the terms by which electronic computers operate, follow a basic technique developed by Bell Laboratories people. The Laboratories also pioneered in developing systems that swiftly transfer a machine from one job to another, give programmers ready access to standard routines, and simplify the programming of engineering and scientific work. Error-detection codes, originally developed in the telephone art, are now routinely employed in the computer industry, and error-correcting codes devised by R. W. Hamming and others at Bell Laboratories

continued on page 115

Herbert E. Ives

The Man Behind
TV Transmission

The first demonstrations of television transmission in the United States were accomplished under the direction of Herbert E. Ives of Bell Laboratories. Their success, nearly half a century ago, rested on the knowledge of electro-optics Ives had acquired during nearly 30 years of study of light, color and vision. From his school days, Ives was fascinated by how it came to pass that things could be seen. Greatly influenced by his father, a man with a passion for photography and optics (and inventor of the process of making halftone printing plates), Ives worked in photography and photoengraving; studied photoelectricity, phosphorescence, the light of the firefly; learned to measure light and color with exactitude; studied how the eye sees flickering images; devised a scientific three-color palette; and was himself a painter of talent.

These were not all of Ives' interests, but they help to explain why, at Bell Laboratories, he was chosen to take the lead in research and development toward the transmission of pictures and television.

First came telephotography. In 1923, Ives and several associates developed a method and apparatus for picture transmission over telephone lines. These were used first at the national political conventions in 1924 and soon afterward, with successive refinements, came into general use. That is said easily but it may be remembered that picture transmission had been the object of experiment for years. Ives and his associates were the first to put together a system that would send pictures rapidly over long lines and reproduce them with good quality.

Close on the heels of picture transmission came television. This meant, as Ives himself later commented, speeding the picture system up so that the result would be "production and transmission of a picture in a fifteenth of a second, instead of seven minutes."

By May 1925, a system of sorts was enabling workers in the laboratory to distinguish a face at the receiving end. Ten months later, with the help of new developments, including a scanning beam devised by Frank Gray, the system was vastly improved but still in the laboratory. On April 7, 1927, however, in an auditorium in New York, guests saw and heard Herbert Hoover, then Secretary of Commerce, on a large screen as he spoke over a telephone line from Washington. This was followed immediately by a program of amateur vaudeville sent by radio to New York from Whippany, New Jersey.

During the next three years Ives and his colleagues demonstrated apparatus that allowed outdoor scenes to be televised in natural light, transmitted television in color, and set up a two-way telephone-television system between two locations in New York City.

Bell Laboratories' interest in all this was not to devise terminal equipment for television broadcasting and reception, but to learn the requirements for transmission over long-distance networks. Ives' work in the 1920's, and his background in photography and photometry, gave Bell engineers a sound basis for designing circuits for television transmission. It also allowed them to develop techniques that would precisely measure the relationship between transmission bandwidth and the quality of the televised image.

Clearly Ives was much involved in development problems. But he was first of all a scientist, and as a scientist he regarded his work on the photoelectric effect—the emission of electrons from metals irradiated with light—as his principal contribution, considered for itself and apart from its importance to television. Studying thin films of alkali metals, Ives found that the emission, in a wide variety of cases, was proportional to the intensity of the "standing wave" in the film; and so he resolved one of the main problems of photoelectricity. These studies, incidentally, extended over many years.

So many were Ives' interests, as tributes written following his death in 1953 reveal, that they cannot be mentioned here even briefly. We shall simply have to leave it that his work in television transmission once again made clear how essential depth of knowledge has been to all advances in communications.

Ives holds one of the photocells used in the first intercity television demonstration on April 7, 1927. At the right is the television screen used in the demonstration.

have been used extensively. The Laboratories was also one of the first organizations to develop digital computer methods for the design, manufacture and maintenance of other digital systems.

In computer graphics—the linking of a computer with display and film-processing equipment—there have been many contributors but it seems fair to say that Bell Laboratories has made some of the most useful advances. These have led to striking results in the production of motion pictures, drawings, patterns and printing. In another aspect, however, they have simply been part of the overall strong effort to develop methods for efficient interaction between people and machines, so that investigators in different fields can examine trial results, perhaps repeatedly, without delay. Visualization aids understanding; and inventive computing science has made this a part of the wide-ranging repertory of schemes, languages, translation methods and techniques designed to help engineers, economists and thinkers throughout the Bell System to use computer-power to the full.

For the same kind of reason—to get the machines widely and efficiently used—Bell Laboratories was early active in efforts to expand time-shared computing. As long ago as 1964 it showed how large computers could be made available over telephone circuits to programmers at typewriter consoles. It also demonstrated how data links could be used for routine monitoring and supervision of computer facilities and for balancing loads on machines at different locations. More recently, Laboratories people have created a time-shared system for minicomputers that can be used for research problems, text editing and the preparation of documents—and also for testing and monitoring telephone switching systems, correlating trouble reports, and alerting repair forces when necessary.

This system reflects the fact that in recent years Bell Laboratories researchers in computing science have pioneered in the study of how to use mini-

computers to best advantage. They have interconnected hardware components from different computer manufacturers, built special-purpose devices to supplement the machines, and devised operating systems that combine the maker's software with programs written by Laboratories people. The result, says S. P. Morgan, who directs the computing science research, has been "more effective computing power than we could possibly have had from a single general-purpose system." What has been achieved essentially is a new flexibility, an ability to tailor-make systems for particular tasks. Thus, for example, one minicomputer system controls the ion-implantation process already mentioned; another is used for the design of integrated circuits; and a third aids the study of economic systems by displaying different functions of time which the researcher can interrelate by typing in equations. In each case, appropriate graphics associated with the system allow the user, as need may require, to monitor the process, perfect design or compare results.

COMPUTER NETWORKS

A logical next step in computing science is the interconnection of computers in high-speed networks. This is further encouraged by the fact that the digital techniques used in computers and switching systems are now extending rapidly into transmission systems. As Dr. Baker has put it, "The language with which information is processed and managed in modern computers is precisely compatible with that which we are employing in . . . the general communication system. Hence individuals can allocate their needs for communication and computer-based information in compatible form in both time and space. This is surely one of the most remarkable combinations in modern science and engineering."*

One computer network experiment at Bell Laboratories can use several loops, each serving

---

*"The Use of Computers in Communications," *ISA Transactions*, Vol. 6, No. 2 (April 1967).

A Bell Laboratories computer researcher is reflected in a cathode-ray tube display of characters from a computer "software" routine she helped develop. The program allows a computer to draw attention to likely misspellings in a manuscript typed into it.

One likely area of usefulness for such networks, says Dr. Morgan, is where a large number of jobs are to be done, each needing, however, only a small amount of computation. In that situation, instead of relying on a single large computer with many distant terminals, it may be far better to use a system of small machines, each designed for a specific job but also able to coordinate with others over a network. One advantage is that the programming is simpler. Also, the cost of building in protection to assure reliability may be much less. And third, it is easy for such a system to grow in modular units.

COMPUTER-BASED RESEARCH

One reason for putting emphasis here on computing science, computer networks and the like is the hard-to-escape sense that along with solid-state technology (of which the modern high-speed computer itself is an offspring), optical communications, and the melding of digital methods in both transmission and switching, they constitute one of the main waves of the future. Already, as the next chapter will show, computer programs are profoundly affecting how the whole communication system is to be planned, designed, built and operated. Already also, the second half of our heading back on page 110—computers in research—could run to unwelcome length, since the amount of research that does not have recourse to computers is minimal. However, we shall not try to cover the waterfront, but limit ourselves to a few instances of how Bell Laboratories scientists are using computers to obtain knowledge and produce results otherwise beyond reach.

Some of these instances, as the reader must have noticed, have already been touched on in the context of *continuity with renewal*. They include the synthesis of speech, investigations of how the human vocal tract and auditory system really work, and the development of methods that enable a computer to identify a telephone caller by comparing his or her speech with speech previously stored in its memory.

several machines. All the loops, in turn, are served by a common switching unit. The computers can time-share the loops (because each machine needs a transmission path for only brief periods) and it looks as though practically instantaneous connections should be possible. Such sharing of what are in effect "party lines" holds down interconnection costs. In order that the machines, which are of various kinds, may talk to each other in a common language, so-called "interface" units are provided. These are themselves types of minicomputers, able to control errors and diagnose troubles, and could be the ancestors of a family of equipment able to link widely different data processors over a broad network.

continued on page 119

Harvey Fletcher

Student of Speech and Hearing

Talking and hearing are what the telephone is for. Harvey Fletcher made it his prime job at Bell Laboratories to learn everything he could about speech and hearing that might help match the telephone system more closely, and also more economically, with human needs and abilities. The results he obtained have had lasting influence. Also, the techniques that he and his associates devised for their studies led directly to high-fidelity recording, sound motion pictures, the first accurate clinical audiometers to measure hearing, and the first electronic hearing aids.

Fletcher made precise measurements to determine the threshold of hearing and its relation to pitch (frequency). He found the least differences of pitch and loudness that a normal ear can perceive. He measured ability to interpret speech sounds correctly under varying conditions of loudness, from the minimum perceptible to the loudest that could be tolerated.

Analyzing speech and music, Fletcher determined what parts of complex sounds are essential to complete perception, and what parts are not. He discovered, for instance, that certain components of speech sounds, or of musical notes, could be omitted without impairing their intelligibility or quality.

In Fletcher's own time at Bell Laboratories (1916-1949), this knowledge was of great value in guiding the development of telephone transmission. It is also fundamental to new developments today. What he accomplished, in essence, was to specify *physically* what is in the voice and what the ears get out of it. Today this understanding can be combined with understanding (from information theory) of how much *information* speech contains and how it can best be coded, in digital form, to go through an electrical circuit.

On such foundations, scientists at Bell Laboratories have been working recently to derive those parts of sound that are intrinsic to meaning and those that are not, and to establish how *little* electrical capability may be needed to transmit fully intelligible and also natural speech. Indications are that as few as 400 cycles might be adequate, compared with the 3000 previously considered the minimum required for good transmission.

How's that again? Well, to accomplish this needs a form of computer processing that recognizes the acoustic redundancy in speech, translates this redundant input into categories that can be sent digitally over the narrow 400-cycle band, and at the receiving end modifies and adds to these categories so that the listener will hear all the frequencies of good old redundant speech.

How this may eventually work out cannot be predicted with certainty, but the very possibility underscores the continuing vitality of Fletcher's work. Without understanding of the first principles of speech, as he elucidated them, a process such as that indicated above could not even be contemplated. The same is true of another present-day effort; i.e., to generate, by computer, wave patterns that are identical to those produced by the human vocal cords and tract. Sucess there, plus the understanding of digital encoding that already exists, could lead to computer-generated speech—good, natural, precise speech—from first principles of waves and digits; to automatic translation; and to many practical applications in the communications system.

Getting back to Fletcher's own time, we ought to say a bit about the ancillary developments of sound movies, electrical recording, and electronic devices to measure hearing. It is true that they grew mainly out of the need to develop instrumentation for research, but this hardly lessens their impact and influence. Noteworthy too is the fact that the first demonstrations of stereophonic sound, both by direct transmission (from Philadelphia to Washington in 1933) and by recording (in New York in 1940) were made by Fletcher and his colleagues with the cooperation of Leopold Stokowski and the Philadelphia Orchestra. Equipment developed under Fletcher's direction enabled a conductor or artist, on playback of an original record, to enhance or modify the sound to achieve variations in effect. And finally, Fletcher's studies of the voice resulted in an artificial larynx that has benefited thousands of people who have lost their vocal cords.

In the early 1920's, the science of acoustics took a giant forward step when Bell Laboratories scientists devised the audiometer, the first instrument for precise determination of hearing acuity. Here, Fletcher conducts a hearing test on school children in 1928.

These results, by the way, have been aided by just such innovations in the configuration of computing systems as outlined above.

Multidimensional scaling (referred to on page 96) also relies on the computer. In the words of J. B. Kruskal, one of the investigators at Bell Laboratories who has been working in the field, multidimensional scaling is "the name for a well-developed class of methods and computer programs which recover a configuration of points from information about the distances between them." Such programs can be applied to analyses of information relating not only to electrical communications but also to psychology, linguistics, archaeology and other fields of study.

A program developed some years ago by Bell Laboratories mathematicians enables a computer to handle algebraic expressions involving 2000 or more terms—problems which by reason of their size are far beyond the capacity of humans. In studies of vision, the computer has been caused to produce abstract images that are totally unrelated to human experience and so provide new tests of human ability to perceive form and depth, with consequent possible new understanding of how visual perception and learning come about. Reference has already been made (see page 110) to a program that made visible, in motion-picture form, the equations of motion of a satellite tumbling and then stabilizing in space. Among other movies generated by computers at Bell Laboratories are those that illustrate the diffusion of atoms or molecules in materials, the making of semiconductor devices, heat-treatment of metals and alloys, dynamic change in the economic performance of the telecommunications business, the design of language, how electromagnetic waves are generated, and the effect of waveguide design changes on performance. This work in computer animation, it may be added, has had considerable impact on other industries, on government (NASA produced motion pictures simulating conditions astronauts might

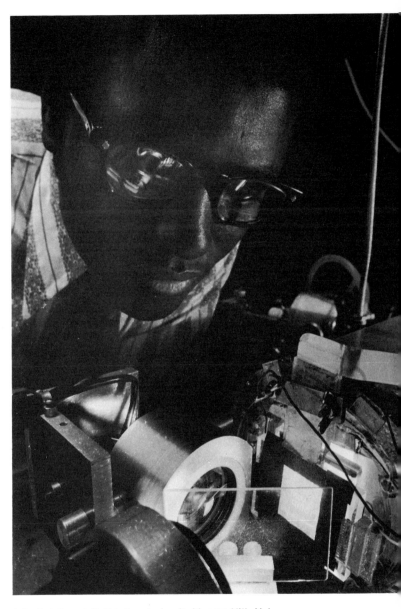

A technician at Bell Laboratories in Murray Hill, N.J., examines the heart of a new liquid-crystal display system, which uses invisible (infrared) light to form images in a liquid crystal and visible light to project the images onto a screen. The technique could be used as an "electronic blackboard" system, as a computer terminal for designing new equipment, or as a manufacturing tool.

Melted by the intense heat of an invisible laser beam, an extremely pure glass rod is drawn out to produce a hair-thin optical fiber. Such fibers may be used within the next few years to transmit telephone conversations on light waves.

encounter) and generally on the production of educational films.

Bell Laboratories research people have used computers to gather and correlate enormous amounts of data on charged particles, gases and molecules in space— a body of knowledge not otherwise obtainable. They have been studying, with computers, the behavior of groups of atoms and single atoms in molecules, even during chemical change. They use computers to make simplified models of elements in enzyme structures, which play a central role in vital processes. They have showed how computers can parse sentences, duplicate type designs, prepare indices, and correct manuscripts. . . But perhaps enough has now been said to make two points.

INSIGHTS AND SKILLS

One is that the purpose of computing at Bell Laboratories, as Dr. Hamming expresses it, has been insight, not numbers. Not every insight can lead to practical application but one can lead to another and the sum of them all makes a great difference. It is the accumulation of knowledge, the slow building of wisdom, the pyramiding of understanding upon understanding, that makes possible a new reach.

The second point is that intensive study and use of computer techniques in the Bell System, as in other organizations, develop a new kind of human facility. To more and more people, using a computer now comes as naturally as using a screwdriver. This is taken for granted at Bell Laboratories. What can never be taken for granted is the ability to devise imaginative inputs and to ask the kinds of questions that computers deserve to be asked. Such questions today relate not only to the "traditional" areas of research in the natural and behavioral sciences but also to the entire subject of how a vast and intricate structure like the Bell System should be operated. This will be touched on in Chapter 9.

Employees in a Bell Laboratories computation center load
programs and data into a large computer installation.
A wide variety of computer assistance is required for
telecommunications research and development. Each
center is accessible round the clock to users at several
locations through remote terminals.

121

1876 Bell's first telephone transmitter (left) and receiver

1877 First commercial telephone

1878 Wall set with two transmitter- receivers

1882 First phone built by Western Electric for Bell System

1886 Long-distance transmitter

1891 Cabinet set the size of a grandfather clock

1897 Cast brass deskstand

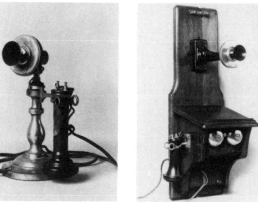

1900 Wall set powered by central office batteries

1907 Wall set with generator to signal operator

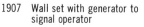

1910 Deskstand, standard for a quarter-century

1919 Deskstand dial telephone

ACCESS TO THE NETWORK

8

The year 1925 marked a major transition point in the evolution of telephones. Up to that time the telephones in common use were the deskstand, popularly called the candlestick set, and a small variety of wall sets.

The idea of having both transmitter and receiver on a common handle to form a handset was not new at that time and a number of models were being used in European countries. However, these handsets were limited in performance. Transmitter efficiency depended on how one held the handset. They tended to produce howling, and the instruments themselves were noisy. In the late 20's, Bell Laboratories engineers designed a radically new and improved transmitter and improved receiver which overcame these problems. These and other advances were incorporated in the Bell System combined set of 1937 (300 type). Almost 30 million of these sets were produced, and they established new standards for good performance, low maintenance and low cost.

The 500 type telephone introduced in 1949, like its predecessor, was the product of years of continuing research and development, utilizing new circuit principles, new materials, and new knowledge of the human factors in telephone usage. This set provided a large gain in transmitter efficiency, an equally large gain in receiver efficiency, and improved speech quality and articulation. Along with improved fidelity, substantial

savings were made possible because the set operated better on higher resistance cable, using less copper. And with all of this came the benefits of reduced maintenance cost, one of the important design objectives. Finally, the set was produced so efficiently by the Western Electric Company that its price to the Bell companies was well below that of any other telephone set available in the entire world. And since then, continuing intensive cost reduction engineering has been effective in offsetting increased labor rates and material costs to further lower the price of our telephones.

The Princess® telephone, introduced in 1959, was an innovative step in miniaturization, with the added feature of an illuminated dial for convenience at night. In 1964, Touch-Tone phones provided simpler and faster dialing than rotary dial phones. Touch-Tone dialing opened the way for new uses of the telephone as a device for transmission of data and access to computer-stored information. A year later the Trimline® telephone appeared—the first modular telephone with its dial in the handset. Subsequent improvements and refinements brought the use of integrated circuits, with their advantages of lower cost and better reliability.

The solid-state art has made possible more sophisticated telephones which can do more for the user. The most recent of these is the Touch-a-matic® repertory dialer, which stores 31 pre-set numbers in its memory and requires only the touch of a single button to dial a call anywhere in the United States. The latest developments in solid-state memory, with integrated circuits and thousands of transistors, make this possible. And there is Picturephone service, the next large step forward in communications, where users can see each other and graphic material like charts, diagrams and printed pages. Picturephone service is still being tested to find its place in business and in the home. In this brief listing, nothing has been said about the continuing succession of new and improved coin telephones, key telephones for business uses, hands-free speakerphones, special telephones for the handicapped and other specialized telephones.

The common theme in 50 years of telephone instrument development at the Laboratories has been concern for performance, reliability and low cost. By continual exploitation of new materials, new circuits and new design techniques, Bell Laboratories, working closely with AT&T, Bell System telephone companies and Western Electric, has produced a comprehensive variety of useful telephones.

1928   Desk set with transmitter and receiver in handset

1937   300 type desk set with bell in base

1958   Call Director® telephone for business offices

1959   Compact Princess telephone with illuminated dial

1968   Trimline telephone with Touch-Tone dialing

1969   Picturephone set provides visual communications

1964   Touch-Tone card dialer telephone

1973   Touch-a-matic telephone dials numbers automatically

124

Key set for handling
several lines

1949 500 type desk set; in color,
1954

1956 Wall set

1958 Speakerphone set for
hands-free conversation

62 Panel telephone mounts
flush with wall

1964 Touch-Tone telephone,
buttons replace rotary dial

1966 Call-a-matic® telephone
stores up to 500 numbers

1966 Single-slot coin
telephone

1974 Design Line™ telephones — some of the
designs are from a non-Bell manufacturer

1974 Modular telephone simplifies
installation and repair

1974 Transaction™ telephone
checks credit data

The latest member of the Bell System's new family of data sets was introduced in 1974 for data communications customers who transmit digital information at a rate of 9600 bits per second. Using the latest integrated circuit electronics, these sets offer improved performance, smaller size and lower cost.

GETTING IT ALL TOGETHER

9

If there is a more complex man-made system than the Bell Telephone network, no one has yet named it. Its component parts are beyond calculation in number. They are also interactive and operate on each other with a speed and subtlety hard to describe. Tough and strong individually, they are yet held in a balance so delicate as to be almost precarious and their interaction, while incessant, cannot be predicted. At any moment, someone who wants to talk will cause thousands of magnets, crystals, tubes, transistors, integrated circuits and other devices to function in a combination never effected before and in all probability never to be repeated, since the next call from the same point of origin to the same destination will almost certainly make its way through a train of connections at least slightly different.

Unpredictable interactions can also cause problems. In an interconnected system, a trouble here can make trouble there. All the more reason, therefore, for precautions, for spares, for redundancy, for continuous surveillance, for automatic substitution when a circuit fails, for "self-auditing" arrangements in electronic switching systems. These auditing systems watch constantly for signs of difficulty and apply the appropriate remedy—one instance among many of what might be called high-technology maintenance.

But complexity is not just a matter of electronics. Services are diverse: talk, pictures, computer communications, data on display a thousand miles from its point of origin. Environments are different too. The subsystems of the total system that serve rural Mississippi cannot be designed in the same way as those that serve metropolitan New York. And many users have special and multiple needs. A full-time voice circuit from an office in New Brunswick, New Jersey, to a warehouse in Long Island City must thread its way via 200 physical connections made by different people in a dozen locations. Or two corporations, each with its favorite bag of communication services, decide to merge. The result: a new lineup altogether and a whole new bag of tricks.

Perhaps that is enough to make the point. The point is that the present-day elaboration of the communications network—a system intricate, protean, and always churning and changing*—demands the application of modern science not merely to the

*Each year one out of every five people in the United States moves.

service-rendering systems of the network, but to the methods by which they are built, operated and maintained. This has inevitably required Bell Laboratories' increasingly deep and intimate involvement in the determination of how the Bell System is to work.

A STETHOSCOPE ON THE NETWORK

How do Bell Laboratories people actually involve themselves in operating affairs? The answer is, in all kinds of ways. In New York City, for instance, a few years ago, when service problems were acute, Laboratories engineers teamed with telephone company people in computer-aided studies that pinpointed the causes of failure. This work led, in turn, to programs that would detect the beginnings of similar problems at other times in other places. The teams analyzed records, located errors, brought hitherto unsuspected equipment deficiencies to light. They studied traffic flows, the mix of voice and data calls, the impact of surges of calls to particular locations.

"In effect," one Bell Laboratories engineer remarked, "we held a stethoscope on the network." And he went on to say, "If we can develop analytical tools now the way we developed hardware in the past, and make them available to the telephone companies, then they will get the analysts they need to use these tools."

Another aspect of Bell Laboratories' role in operations is the monitoring of new systems as they come into use. For instance, Laboratories engineers are "on line," literally, with every new electronic central office installation. If problems are encountered, they help the telephone company to deal with them at once. Such monitoring is not limited to switching systems, of course; Bell Laboratories people have a follow-through responsibility with every new design.

THE LOOP PLANT

A third aspect of operational teamwork is found in

continued on page 131

A Bell Laboratories study was conducted with Southwestern Bell in Dallas, 1972, to compare the performance of directory assistance operators using conventional telephone directories with the performance of operators using microfilm. This was one of several studies aimed at making directory assistance more efficient and more responsive to customers' needs.

Walter A. Shewhart

Pioneer in Quality Control Engineering

On May 16, 1924, Dr. Walter A. Shewhart wrote a note to the head of Western Electric Company's inspection engineering department (soon to be a part of Bell Laboratories). He enclosed, he said, "a form of report designed to indicate whether or not the observed variations in the per cent of defective apparatus of a given type are significant; that is, to indicate whether or not the product is satisfactory."

The enclosure was the first "Shewhart Control Chart," based on principles that have caused their creator to be described as the founder of statistical quality control or, in the words of Professor C. C. Craig of the University of Michigan, as "truly the father of scientific process control."

As Shewhart himself said in the memorandum quoted above, the theory underlying his proposals was "somewhat involved." In the next several years he developed the theory in what has been generally recognized as the classic text on the subject of quality control.

Shewhart's *Economic Control of Quality of Manufactured Product* was published in 1931. In this "great book," wrote Professor Irving W. Burr, "the whole field was laid out including its theory, philosophy, applications, and most pertinently, its economic aspects. Few fields of knowledge have ever been so completely explored and charted in the first exposition." Nevertheless Shewhart continued to explore the field further in many papers and lectures, some of which became another book, *Statistical Method from the Viewpoint of Quality Control,* published in 1938.

A third observer of Shewhart's contributions, Professor Frederick F. Stephan of Princeton University, has commented that as mass production methods were developed in American industry, "Walter Shewhart worked with insight, rigorous thinking and persistence to pioneer the methods of economic and statistical quality control that were needed. Indeed, when the defense program that preceded our entry into World War II rapidly accelerated these industrial developments, Shewhart's methods were ready for use throughout the defense industries and they provided the foundation for the rapid development of quality control engineering that culminated in the foundation of the American Society for Quality Control."

Use of Shewhart's control charts, and of the theory that underlies them, has extended around the world. One more quotation—this one from a former colleague and life-long friend, Harold F. Dodge—may help to suggest why. The control chart, Dodge thought, set up a sort of Utopian goal. Is it an attainable goal? "Perhaps not perfectly," Dodge wrote, "but the production man could try. The control chart could tell him what went wrong and when, and enable him to improve his process. And the goal was something which, in the seeking, would result in removing wasteful causes of variation in quality, and lead to a more trouble-free and hence more economical process. Finally, the control chart provided a basis for determining when he had attained statistical control. With these things in mind, Shewhart developed the meaning of three aspects of statistical control—as a concept, as an operation, and as a judgment."

As a concluding indicator of Shewhart's influence, it may be remarked that the quotations above have been selected from comments by some 30 leaders in the field, all published in *Industrial Quality Control,* the journal of the American Society for Quality Control, in August 1967, the year of Shewhart's death.

Here, in 1955, Shewhart (middle), whose contribution included pioneering work in quality control, talks with colleagues V. Michael Wolontis (left) and Edward Kaplan.

what is commonly called (by telephone people) the loop.

Of all communications terminology, this is perhaps the most misleading. It sounds so simple. And it is not! For loop plant is everything between the telephone exchange and the customer. It starts on a frame where wires from the dial switches are connected to electronic circuits and to wires that go into cables that go under streets and through manholes and up into apartments and offices and factories and universities and museums and banks and airports and whatever. Everybody's telephone is on the loop. So are a hundred thousand private branch exchanges and a hundred thousand Dataphone data sets and heaven knows how many computers. The loop is where lines are assigned and repair service people answer calls for help and installers and repairmen drive their trucks. In short, the loop is a very big place, representing an investment for the Bell System alone of about $20 billion. It also has what economists coolly call a high labor content and this makes it, nowadays, very expensive to run.

For such reasons, the loop is the scene of intensive examination and activity to redesign both physical equipment and ways of working, introduce new features, cut costs and improve service. The story is too long for telling here, but it is important to note that many of the new devices and systems referred to on previous pages, and later in this chapter, are specifically directed toward more efficient design, construction and operation of loop plant. And as one result, concomitantly with service improvement, Bell Laboratories engineers confidently expect the present worth of savings over the next ten years to come to about $2 billion.

NEW SCIENCE FOR NEW NEEDS

"The Bell System," says President Baker, "is a vast operational entity and we have found that operational technology is much more profound than had been assumed. But praise be, to help direct it we also now have new science, new math, new data management, new information analysis; and we are finding that this science of today holds as great promise for present Bell System needs and opportunities as the hardware-creating science of the first half of the century held in its time.

"How do you forecast needs, plan construction, lay out routes, locate switching, control inventories, handle complicated orders, and manage and maintain systems in optimal fashion? These and a hundred other such questions constitute the overwhelming scientific and technical problem for the next several years in making the Bell System go. Sure, work of this kind has always had to be done. But the problems are far bigger and more pressing today than they used to be and they need the new science, which fortunately we have been building and, I am certain, can apply with success."

Question: Is this systems engineering? Or operations research? And Baker answers, "Well, perhaps both —but if it's operational research, it's that on a new scale and it also goes way beyond the old systems engineering, although it includes it."

MAINTENANCE MACHINES

The "old" systems engineering, which was born in the 1920's at AT&T and grew up there and at Bell Laboratories, is a topic in itself and we shall get to it later. First, however, let us take a wider look at what Baker calls operational technology and show by example some of the efforts being made to advance it. We can begin with the fact that all these myriad interconnected and interconnecting parts have to be repeatedly tested and continuously maintained. What is the "new science" helping to do about that?

One instance is a system to improve the maintenance of trunk lines. There are now over five and a half million of these (up more than one-third of a million from a year ago) and the expectation is that ten years hence there will be many, many more. Looking after them, therefore, is a big essential job that gets

Engineers test a preliminary model of the CAROT (Centralized Automatic Reporting on Trunks) system at the Holmdel, N.J., location of Bell Laboratories. The system automatically tests telephone trunk lines which interconnect central offices, and prints out reports on the condition of the lines.

on reams of paper. Today a computer system can analyze the tests, separate out unimportant results, and warn of others that may cause trouble. Hence maintenance people can concentrate on problems that are important instead of chasing details that are not.

A third system designed to improve maintenance controls the analysis of troubles experienced in long-distance switching machines and in so-called "tandem" machines that interconnect local central offices in metropolitan areas (instead of every local office having to be directly connected with every other). Two such systems, serving San Francisco and Los Angeles, receive and correlate reports from 40 machines and make possible much faster trouble-shooting at much lower cost. For those who relish computer language, these systems rejoice in the name of Computer-Aided Reorder Trap Analysis, or CARTA for short. More importantly, they derive from Bell Laboratories pioneering in minicomputer arrangements (page 115) and represent but one application of a system that can be variously adapted for use in research, in testing other systems and in administration.

FROM PLANNING TO OPERATIONS . . .

Many other systems in widening use and under development cover a range of engineering, construction and network planning problems as well as minute-to-minute operational maintenance. One of the most important deals with the essential task of engineering additions to central office switching equipment as the number of telephone customers grows. Detailed information on more than 2500 central offices is already stored in this system, and engineers in telephone companies all across the country are "consulting" it about 5000 times a month for help in planning equipment additions.

Other systems help engineers decide where new central offices should be located and what size cables should be placed along what routes, and on what

bigger every day. The system we are speaking of initiates tests automatically and more frequently than is possible by hand, analyzes the results and gives immediate notice of trouble spots. As now developing, this CAROT system (short for Centralized Automatic Reporting on Trunks) includes a control center for each area having roughly 100,000 trunks. It also makes some very healthy demands on people. This is because the numbers (the data base, in computer terms) are always changing and this requires careful attention to keep records up to date.

Here is another example. Any modern switching machine pours out the results of line-insulation tests schedule. Another is used in evaluating alternatives in building construction, taking into account, among other things, tax rates, capital structure, capital needed, operating and maintenance costs, depreciation practice and the effect of economic inflation. Another brings to a central point information on groups of switching machines, not only to allow centralized maintenance through remote controls but to facilitate network management and planning.

A system now on trial will, it is believed, revolutionize the whole procedure for making cross-connections between customers' lines and central office switches. Still another is accomplishing fundamental change in the efficiency of repair service bureaus where it has been installed. For instance, this system enables the person who answers a customer's call for help to determine instantly, without having to refer the problem to a technician, just what the difficulty is (or whether it still exists, for many reported troubles clear themselves in minutes or less).

MULTIPLE IMPACTS

These and other systems based on the new science of information processing and analysis have more than one kind of impact. They are pointed toward service improvement, greater reliability, more accurate records and better control of costs. And the payoffs can be large.

For example, the telephone companies use many millions of circuit packs and other small equipment assemblies that are plugged into switching and transmission systems for all sorts of purposes—to replace other units, expand or modify services, and whatnot. An inventory management system that keeps track of local stocks of every variety of plug-in equipment has already been tried out in two Bell operating companies and promises savings not in millions of dollars but in hundreds of millions over the next ten years.

Here is another big saver:

A major element of the communications system is

To help telephone companies respond to customer requests for changes in service, Bell Laboratories developed a computer-based message-handling system. Telephone companies use the system, named BISCOM (for Business Information Systems Communications), to store information in a central data base and speed it to installation, accounting, directory and other departments.

of course the vast network of trunk circuits, both long and short, that tie together all central offices. This trunk plant does not stay permanently in the same configuration but is constantly being rearranged as it grows. Keeping track of these changes requires thousands of record-keepers, and when the work is done by hand it is open to errors that can cause circuits to be literally lost in the shuffle.* A computer system is gradually being extended, therefore, to integrate the records of all Bell System trunk circuits. Savings of at least several hundred millions over a ten-year period are expected to result from lower labor costs, recovery of "lost" circuits, and a better, more accurate job in the future.

Still another system of comparable potential size and influence is directed toward precise specification and guidance of the several kinds of work that must be done when a customer orders service. What line will be assigned and what telephone number? What details of information will help the installer do his job without delay? Exactly where should the craft people in the central office make the connection?

*See the comment on record-keeping for the CAROT system, page 132.

133

The answers to these and other questions will be specified so that the employees concerned will know exactly what to do; and in order also that each installation will be made in such a way that the load on the exchange's facilities will be evenly balanced.

This is perhaps also the place to recall again that how well computer-based systems will work depends on how well they are designed to interact with people and on the qualifications and training of the people who design, install and use them. Each system is a combination of machines and human beings. An important part of Bell Laboratories' role in helping to build the new operational technology, therefore, is to develop methods, courses and training aids for both its own people and those of the telephone companies who are working together to bring new systems into the operating environment. In addition, psychologists at Bell Laboratories' "human performance technology center" work to understand causes of error and fatigue so that these causes can be designed out of the systems.

ADVANTAGES AND PROBLEMS

Question: May not computer systems concerned with different aspects of the same subject tend to come together? The answer is indeed yes—and this very fact can add value. Thus, a system that analyzes trends in the growth of communications traffic and circuit rearrangements, in order to aid forecasting (and such a system is being developed), can feed useful data to a system that integrates all trunk line records.

However, multiplicity can also cause problems. Some of the most used and useful computer programs in the Bell System have not come from Bell Laboratories but have originated in the telephone companies, and there is little doubt that this aspect of the process of "getting it all together" has had its share of growing pains. In this connection, Eric Sumner, who is in charge of Bell Laboratories work to improve the design, construction and operation of loop plant,

has observed, "We really need a master program to help the telephone companies make the right decisions about which programs to use to do the total job." The implication is not that the telephone companies should leave the job to Bell Laboratories. Sumner was simply saying that if the Laboratories had done more sooner there might have been less heterogeneity for all concerned to resolve. Yet local initiatives remain essential. As the late Julius Molnar once said when he was Bell Laboratories' executive vice president, "It is not our function to hand-hold the companies"—a comment one can be sure any telephone company president will hurry to agree with.

What this all comes down to is the necessity for continuous cooperative endeavor among telephone company and Bell Laboratories people. The more widely standard systems can be applied to meet local needs, the greater their usefulness. Some Bell Laboratories computer programs, as it happens, are based on local programs with modifications to make them useful in other areas too. Regardless of where an idea starts, if it can be developed for nationwide application, it may yield tremendous economies along with service improvement. It may be said too that the systems instanced above, along with numerous others, constitute the most exacting joint effort ever applied to Bell System operations. The computer, as so many have learned to their consternation, poses stringent intellectual demands; and so it has come about that the very tools available have demanded thorough analysis by scientists, engineers and operating managers together.

The above simply says what one repeatedly hears from those concerned. In the first chapter of this book mention is made of the self-critical feeling of some at Bell Laboratories for not having sooner grasped the need for their involvement in operational problems. Jack Baird, who was in charge of systems engineering and, later, network planning at Bell Laboratories before going to AT&T in 1973 as engineering vice president, has put it that the dazzling

A system developed by Bell Laboratories for Bell telephone companies improves service, controls costs and streamlines record-keeping in preparation of customer telephone directories. The two-foot length of magnetic tape shown here holds listings from one page of a directory. Some 300,000 listings, enough to fill the white pages of the directory for a large city, can be stored on two reels of tape.

attraction of new technology led to a tardiness in realizing that high priority would have to be given to making older equipment work better. And Molnar once shrewdly said, "The trouble was, engineering didn't deal with used installations—only new. The old was *plant*"—that is, the old was just something there, not quite so worthy of a Bell Laboratories engineer's tender, loving care.*

Not, to repeat, that he could do it all. "The fact is," says President Baker, "that neither our people nor those in the telephone companies know enough separately to handle the job. They have to pool their

---

*While the Bell System is of course only one of many businesses challenged to find ways of using computer systems wisely in pursuit of improved operations, the size, diversity and interactive character of the communications network present exceptional and often unique problems.

brains and experience." And the same thought is echoed by Bell Laboratories engineers committed to the joint operation. Says one, "In my group we are working to redevelop and restructure a line of plant maintenance and administrative procedures in the form of software all the companies can use. One result we look for is that for the first time they will be able to deal with testing and maintenance over wide areas on a standard basis. But to accomplish this we have to work hand in hand with the telephone company people—there is no other way."

SYSTEMS ENGINEERING OLD AND NEW

Dr. Baker was quoted earlier as saying that the new science includes the "old" systems engineering but goes beyond it. To understand that, let us take a look at the old and then assess what may be new—bearing in mind that if as many as 800 members of Bell Laboratories' technical staff are systems engineers, it must be for a pretty good reason.

Systems engineering was never invented. As remarked earlier, it was born at AT&T in the 1920's, when communications technology and systems were already getting quite complicated, and grew up in Bell Laboratories. Estill Green, who had charge of it at Bell Laboratories in the 1950's, once said the term reminded him of the mayapple, so named, he thought, because it looks like a lemon and ripens in July. A better term, in Green's view, would have been development planning, although he agreed that the "systems" part was probably all right since the planning usually had to do with more systems than one and how they would function together.

At any rate, Green's *development planning* makes immediately clear the original function, which was—and still is—to study and plan the possible introduction of new technological developments. Such studies cover many questions. What technical developments are needed and what is possible? What new knowledge must we get to fill a gap? Among alternative developments, which may be

This Private Branch Exchange (PBX) was developed at Bell Laboratories in 1972 to serve customers whose businesses require 300 to 2000 telephone lines. It was designed as part of a full range of PBX's with various service packages tailored to a variety of business needs.

best for a particular purpose? And what are the economics? Those are a few of them.

Such study is essential before commitment is made to the large costs of a specific development. And appraisal can lead to various answers. Perhaps new capabilities can best be applied in some new service or system; or, alternatively, perhaps an existing system can be improved, or its cost reduced, or both; or it may be smart, for a while anyway, to mark time. Systems engineering* must also define the nature and extent of risks; recommend standards; keep standards and costs in balance; and if and when

*It is thought that the term "systems engineering" originated with G. W. Gilman of Bell Laboratories—who, by the way, gave the first college course on the subject in 1948, at Massachusetts Institute of Technology.

a development comes into being, look to see that it is doing what it is supposed to do. In sum, systems engineering pulls together knowledge from operations, research and development.

Some of the most interesting questions for systems engineers in recent years have had to do with the extension of digital transmission systems, which carry information in streams of coded pulses (Chapter 3), and with the introduction of long-distance switching machines that make connections according to when the pulses are slotted in time (Chapter 6). Digital transmission, to repeat, has many advantages—easy regeneration of pulses, ability to handle words, data and pictures in any desired mix, efficiency on short trunk lines, compatibility with computers, compatibility also with the new switching systems mentioned in the preceding sentence. Further, as we have also seen, the oncoming high-capacity "millimeter wave" systems must by their very nature be digital, whether the waves are guided through a tube or beamed through the air. Yet most existing long-distance systems today are not digital but analog, for the very good reason that they are more efficient that way.

So—how important is it to move digitally—in what directions—and how fast? The task of the systems engineer is to study and weigh all the factors. His computer is at hand and he uses it to build models. Some of the model-making materials are: Projected increases in various kinds of traffic year by year. Comparative capabilities and costs of different kinds of transmission systems. The outlook for switching developments and costs. Industrial trends and geographical considerations.

Then he can begin to examine what the network may look like some years hence, in terms of what facilities will be where, and the dates when the first few time-division switching systems will be ready for regional interconnection; digital islands, one might say, in the analog ocean. Then he can ask, "When will traffic and economy allow cross-country inter-connection of these digital islands? The first transcontinental waveguide? The first from north to south?"

All this is rudimentary. The broad study must also be divided into its parts and each part be given its own systems-engineering scrubbing. What performance objectives should be established? What new services may become practical? What problems must be dealt with at the interfaces with other systems? And maintenance: can ways be devised to monitor performance over wide areas from central points, to detect troubles and remove and restore circuits automatically, to cut maintenance costs?

WIDENING BOUNDARIES

It will be noticed at this point that the systems engineer's concern extends deep into the way the new kind of system is to operate in conjunction with the old, and that integration of research and development with operations is in truth the central

necessity. No part of the system can be considered apart from the rest of it, and new and old alike should meet overall performance standards. Hence, for example, to paraphrase part of an "official" summary of what systems engineering is all about, "systems studies analyze operating environments, metropolitan area networks and switching plans, rural communications, demographic considerations, and more, and establish suitable methods for design, operation and maintenance."

That is a stiff institutional way of saying that systems engineering is up to its neck in problems of operational technology, just as Dr. Baker said. Or one may put it that under the circumstance of increasing complexity in communications on the one hand, and increasing computer power on the other, the boundaries of systems engineering practice are a lot wider than they used to be. While historically the systems engineering function has related mainly to the introduction and evaluation of new technology

A systems engineer at Bell Laboratories explains traffic studies that show how the Bell System network can be used more effectively. In such studies, information about calls through the network is stored on magnetic tape and analyzed by computer.

(and this function of course remains), now comes the overwhelming need to coordinate and improve all phases of construction, operation and maintenance in a fast-changing art. Inevitably, therefore, much systems engineering today has a strongly operational cast, and systems thinking—by whatever name it is called—marvelously challenged and stimulated by the computer, is reflected in scores of operational programs.

QUALITY ASSURANCE

One more phase of Bell Laboratories' involvement in operational technology belongs under this chapter heading. This is quality assurance. A note elsewhere in this book (page 129) about Dr. Walter Shewhart, who laid the foundations for statistical methods of quality control, attests to Bell Laboratories' long-standing concern in the field. The point we make here is that, while the methods Shewhart pioneered have spread all over the world, the specific commitment and procedure followed in the Bell System are still unique. The sum of it is that Bell Laboratories maintains an organization that takes responsibility for the quality of design *and manufacture* of products produced for the telephone companies by Western Electric, not only when they are delivered but throughout their service life.

The telephone companies, therefore, do not need to have acceptance organizations to test and approve Western Electric equipment delivered to them. Actually, however, they get a lot more than they could possibly get from having acceptance organizations of their own—for Bell Laboratories establishes the standards Western Electric must meet and has veto control over its output. Product quality is inspected by scientific sampling methods at many stages of the manufacturing process, and once in the field, equipment and systems are subject to sophisticated analysis to verify the quality both of the equipment and its installation. Bell Laboratories field representatives "on location"

with the telephone companies help to enforce the quality assurance commitment. They are on the spot to study problems, find out what may be wrong, and start action to correct it.

A few comments here from Ren Peoples, a Bell Laboratories engineer who was a field representative for several years, are enlightening.

"Field representatives are ambassadors, technical consultants and quality engineers, all three," he said in conversation recently. "I can give you an example of each.

"First, the telephone company I was working with had—and still has—a crucial problem in providing rural service. This has demanded very close cooperative effort to get costs down. I was continuously involved in bringing the teams together and helping to organize the attack. You might say I was a catalyst and interpreter. This rural problem isn't solved by a long shot but some real progress is being made.

"Second is the consulting example. The telephone company had some big customers who were unhappy about the service they were getting through a relatively new kind of equipment. First I listened hard at some company meetings. Then I arranged for Bell Laboratories people to come down and help analyze what was wrong. The upshot was that we found and cleared up problems for which we all shared responsibility.

"The third example has to do with quality engineering. In many business phones we use a little 10-volt lamp. It costs less than a quarter but every time a repairman has to make a visit to replace one that has burned out, the visit costs nearly as many dollars as the lamp costs pennies. So the company thought it was having to spend too much for maintenance. I collected hundreds of lamps that had had to be replaced and sent them to the Laboratories for analysis. I also had lamp voltages measured in many installations and found the voltages were generally higher than the design called for. So there was an environmental problem.

"Now, in this case you have a plain difference of view between the telephone company and the people who design and make the lamps. The company wants longer life and who can really blame them? Not that the Laboratories is sitting on its hands—in fact, right now we are developing something new that we hope will solve the problem. The point is, in this instance, that the field representative was able to focus attention on the need to hurry up that development, and that is what is happening right now."

Field representatives have been on the job since before Bell Laboratories was organized, but their work as catalysts, to use Mr. Peoples' word, seems particularly important in today's complex Bell System. In this role they bring the talents of Laboratories specialists to bear on tough operating problems, and they also carry back to the Laboratories practical appraisals of how good a job is being done to meet the telephone companies' deep concerns. Through such give-and-take, improvements in one place can be extended wherever they may have application.

WHAT PRICE SUCCESS?

To conclude this chapter, one may venture that its heading has more than one meaning. We have been looking at some of the work aimed at bringing together in a more orderly and efficient way the multitude of piece parts that compose the physical Bell System; at the bringing together, also, of the new knowledge and methods at work in what Dr. Baker has called the new science. Most striking, however, anyway, to one observer, has been the coming together of Bell Laboratories, Western Electric and telephone operating people in much closer teamwork.

Will it all succeed? Probably not. But it is hard to doubt that a lot of it will. For a thought to end with

here, another one from Eric Sumner comes to mind.

"What Bell Laboratories people must be sure of," he says, "is that they are tackling the important problems. That matters more than being successful every time. If you are always successful, perhaps you haven't been adventurous enough."

A Bell Laboratories field representative (left) observes a telephone company cable splicer and a staff engineer using new splicing techniques. Field representatives located at Bell System telephone companies act as consultants and liaison agents who keep Laboratories development groups informed about problems with Laboratories-designed equipment.

Bell Laboratories and Western Electric engineers monitor
guidance equipment during a 1960 rocket launch at Cape
Canaveral. The Laboratories radio command guidance
system is probably the world's most reliable. Between 1959
and mid-1974, it guided 412 launches with only seven
failures—none caused by the Laboratories/Western Electric
missileborne guidance equipment.

FOR NATIONAL DEFENSE

10

The fundamental contribution of communications research and development to national security is also the most obvious: it is the technology itself, from which the whole art and system of communications are fashioned. This is a basic resource in peace and war. Bell Laboratories' contribution to the country's strength, therefore, may be judged essentially according to one's view of what it has done to establish and advance communications and electronics technology. Perhaps it should be repeated also that communications have been indispensable to military competence from time immemorial, and leadership in the art carries with it great responsibility.

The responsibility has several aspects. One is to make knowledge available whenever, and often before, the government asks for it; the general practice at Bell Laboratories has always been to keep the government informed of developments that may have significance from the defense standpoint. A good example was the action taken by the Laboratories, on its own initiative, to make full information immediately available to the Department of Defense regarding

invention of the transistor and the results of exploratory development.

Another responsibility is to adapt to military purposes equipment and systems originally developed for normal peacetime use. In World War I days, for instance, the emerging use of vacuum tubes for radiotelephone transmission was instantly important to the Army and Navy, and a great deal of laboratory work centered on efforts to produce good tubes for military use. In those years came the first use of the radiotelephone from shore to battleship, from airplane to ground and ground to air, and between airplanes in flight and submarine chasers at sea. In France, Bell System battalions in the United States Army Signal Corps, using Bell-developed equipment, helped to organize communications for the Allied armies that were generally agreed to be a long step ahead of anything that had been available before.

WORLD WAR II

Following World War I, Bell engineers kept in touch with the Army and Navy regarding defense needs,

Here, a soldier uses a World War II field artillery radio set that made it possible for forward observers to direct the fire of howitzer batteries. In developing these sets, Bell Laboratories drew upon many years of experience in aircraft and mobile radio research and in quartz-crystal frequency control.

Laboratories' effort (with an enlarged work force) was directed to meet them.

"The science underlying electrical communications," said the AT&T annual report for 1941, "is at the very heart of modern war." However one may feel about this, it is a fact that cannot be ignored. Some of Bell Laboratories' most promising science in the 1930's, for instance (wholly peace-oriented!), had showed the potential of the waveguide and had also led to ultra-high-frequency radio transmission techniques. Both were essential to radar development, which became the Laboratories' largest single war-time activity.* Other techniques and skills, based on knowledge of magnetic and other materials, acoustics and electronics, were also rapidly applied to military ends.

Flight trainers for the Navy evolved from many of the same devices that were used in developing telephone central-office dial equipment. Metallurgical studies lengthened the life of gun barrels; research in acoustics and in the properties of crystals made possible improved sonar systems for submarine detection; and years of research in magnetism produced another submarine-locating system in which a sensitive device, trailed over water from an airplane, registers any change in the earth's magnetic field caused by an underwater magnetic body. Similarly, magnetic mine fuses employed magnetic materials that had been developed at Bell Laboratories over the years.

Bell Laboratories shared also in developing rocket-guidance systems, fire-control equipment, acoustic torpedoes and proximity fuses—all of them basically problems in communications. The radars designed at the Laboratories were used on the ground, in systems for the control of naval gunfire, in submarines and in aircraft. Communications equipment included portable information centers for control of air

and various equipment items, especially in the field of radio communication, were designed or adapted for possible military use. However, the country generally was little occupied with such matters until World War II. Then extreme pressure was put on Bell Laboratories, not only to design equipment systems for military communications, but to use its by then highly advanced expertise in electronics to develop complex systems for control of the weapons of war. These needs were critical, and so it came about that in a very short time four-fifths of all Bell

---

*Western Electric produced, from Bell Laboratories' designs, about half of all U.S. radar manufactured in the war years.

operations; radio systems for planes, tanks and mobile artillery, as well as for a worldwide military telegraph service; telephone instruments for talking in planes and tanks; battle-announcing loudspeaker systems; and components and instruments resistant to the damps and mildews of the jungle. The Bell Laboratories School for War Training, organized at the request of the military, trained thousands of officers in how to teach the proper use and maintenance of communications and weapons systems.

All told, Bell Laboratories handled about 1200 major projects for the Army, Navy and National Defense Research Committee. The whole story would take too long for telling in a book not too heavy to hold, let alone in a single chapter, but one development not yet mentioned merits at least a

paragraph. This was the M9 gun director, precursor of guidance systems developed for antiaircraft and antiballistic missiles after the war.

The Army in 1940 called on Bell Laboratories to develop an improved system for control of anti-aircraft fire. "We proposed," President Buckley of the Laboratories wrote later, "an electrical solution of a task which was being performed by a mechanical

In 1939, Bell Laboratories engineers, using directional waveguide antennas, bounced radio waves off ships in New York's upper bay and received the reflections. This technique was first discovered by British scientists and eventually became known as radar. The Laboratories' experiments were one phase of a broad research effort to understand high-frequency waves. In World War II, this research enabled Bell Laboratories to make pioneering contributions to radar technology. Later, it led to development of microwave radio relay systems for long-distance telephone and TV transmission.

device. This solution makes use of electronic tubes and circuits and of other components developed originally for communication purposes and its success is now fully proved . . . It played an important role at the Anzio beachhead, again in Normandy, and its latest triumph has been the part it has played in shooting down robot bombs in England."

POSTWAR SYSTEMS

The M9 gun director was a conspicuous instance of the increasing use of electronic command and control systems in warfare. After World War II, as the United States Government moved to build defenses against possible attack, Bell Laboratories was asked to work on various complex systems to warn of the approach of submarines, aircraft or ballistic missiles and to guide (in earlier years) the NIKE antiaircraft missiles, the Titan ICBM, and currently the antimissile missiles of the SAFEGUARD system. In most of these projects Western Electric has been the prime contractor, with Bell Laboratories responsible for system design and development. In all instances many subcontractors (sometimes hundreds) were involved.

Other large postwar projects in which the Laboratories' skills have been enlisted may be mentioned briefly. The Distant Early Warning (DEW) Line, a chain of radar stations in the far north, was built in the 1950's to warn of possible bombing attack from that direction. "White Alice" was the name given to a "tropospheric scatter" microwave radio system for linking Alaskan and DEW Line stations with command headquarters. The Ballistic Missile Early Warning System (BMEWS), for which Bell Laboratories designed communication facilities reaching thousands of miles back from outlying radars to defense command centers, was and is just what its name describes. The Laboratories also designed communications for the Semi-Automatic Ground Environment (SAGE) system, another warning network, which was devised primarily to alert continental air defenses against attacking aircraft.

Two major systems designed for the Navy were for shipboard use. One, a digital data communications system, enables an aircraft carrier to maintain simultaneous two-way communications with as many as 100 planes in the air. The other coordinates ship defenses and controls defensive fire against multiple attack by planes and missiles. A third sea warfare system, also defensive in character, uses detection devices, coaxial cables, underwater repeaters, and specially designed terminals—all laid on the ocean floor—to provide continuous surveillance of large ocean areas far from United States shores. And an overall communication network for the Department of Defense, called Autovon (for Automatic Voice Network), links installations here and abroad and embraces some particularly sophisticated electronic switching and transmission systems, with specially arranged secrecy and priority features and special arrangements also to protect and insure continuity of service.*

THE POLICY POSITION

All of the above has been understated to avoid repetition of "oohs" and "ahs" about how remarkable such systems are. There is no doubt that they are extremely so, but it is enough to say it once. The SAFEGUARD system in particular has been described as being of almost unimaginable sophistication. Most people, however, are less concerned with its technological virtuosity than with the fundamental question of whether it should exist at all. On this basic point, the position of Bell Laboratories has always been that this is for the government, and ultimately the electorate, to decide. The function of a technical agency should be no more and no less than to do what it is capable of doing if the country wants it done.

---

*The SAGE system previously mentioned is also integrated with Autovon.

This means not only that the Laboratories should accept government decisions. It also means it should not venture to influence them, except as careful studies of what the technology can accomplish—and of its limitations—may be required by government in reaching conclusions. "Influence" in the sense of attempting to sway decisions is simply not permissible.

In any case, Bell Laboratories appears to have little motive for trying to exercise influence. "The fact is," says President Baker, "we have plenty to do without beating a single bush for military work. I'll never say we begrudge the time and effort defense jobs take, but there is no denying that they have sometimes slowed down the things we want to do for the Bell System. Also, people who are familiar with the way these projects are handled know that the great bulk of the work is done by subcontractors. Our task is mainly to supply the expertise (that is where the pinch comes), organize the knowledge, spread it around, keep on top of the total job and take the responsibility."

Since weapons as well as those who command them must now function through complex systems, skills in systems engineering have become essential to military capability. Bell Laboratories' long experience with the necessities of system planning is another main reason, therefore, why government has so often called on the Laboratories for assistance. (Just a glance back through the projects mentioned above will remind the reader of their predominantly systems character.) One might say, in fact, with some oversimplification, that the combination of systems experience and depth of knowledge in electronics put Bell Laboratories, in past years, in a unique position. Today the picture is rather different. Many companies have acquired great skill in electronics and experience also with the systems discipline (although perhaps more of the first than the second). For such reasons it is expected that defense needs in this area will depend relatively less

Developed by Bell Laboratories, the M9 gun director of World War II tracked the path of an enemy plane and gave firing signals to antiaircraft guns. In 1944, M9's brought down 76 per cent of the V-1 "buzz bombs" flying through sectors they defended in England. The M9 control system — the first use of an all-electronic analog computer — drew heavily on Laboratories expertise in telephone switching and circuit design.

on Bell Laboratories in the future than in the past.

Space exploration also exemplifies what has just been said with respect to both systems engineering and depth of knowledge. It is appropriate to mention it here, in the context of Bell Laboratories' role in defense, since guidance systems for space vehicles, and also satellite surveillance systems, are both of fundamental military importance.

On the research or "depth of knowledge" side, the fact is just this broad—that all space vehicle guidance, all satellites, and all space exploration have depended on the discovery and development of the transistor at Bell Laboratories.

On the systems engineering side, the Laboratories'

Radar antennas on the battleship *U.S.S. Alabama* reflect the important role of radar in World War II. Awarding the Medal of Merit to Western Electric's President Clarence G. Stoll in 1946, President Harry S Truman said, ". . . his company produced more than 30 per cent of all electronics and communications equipment and more than 50 per cent of all radar manufactured in this country during the war." Bell Laboratories designed all of this equipment.

role has included the planning of Project Mercury— the first undertaking of the National Aeronautics and Space Administration to place a manned vehicle in orbit—development of Mercury's communications network and control center, design of the Goddard Space Flight Center in Maryland, and much of the organization of communications at and between NASA's Houston and Cape Canaveral installations. As the space program proceeded toward the Apollo phase and the critical problems involved in voyaging to the moon, NASA again turned to the Bell System for assistance. In response, under Bell Laboratories leadership, a small company given the name of Bellcomm, Inc., was organized to provide systems engineering support. Obviously, getting men to the moon and back would be an immensely costly as well as difficult job. It was essential therefore to set optimum objectives; to plan things so that the astronauts would get to the right places on the moon at the right time; to make each visit as productive as possible; to have alternatives available; and so on. It was for such reasons that NASA sought Bell Laboratories' help. Bellcomm worked for 10 years, and when the Apollo program was successfully concluded, the Bell group returned to Bell Laboratories.

One more contribution to defense should be noted. More than 25 years ago the Atomic Energy Commission asked the Bell System to manage the commission's undertaking, conducted mainly at Sandia, New Mexico, and Livermore, California, to design, fabricate, produce and store atomic weapons. David E. Lilienthal, then chairman of the commission, wrote later that the Bell System was asked to do this because "capabilities of research, industrial techniques and operation had to be combined in the same team, with experience in working together as a unit."

The Bell System accepted the assignment, although as Lilienthal also wrote, "it did not relish another great load such as this," and a new Western Electric

146

When the U. S. Air Force installed the Distant Early Warning (DEW) Line across the top of the North American continent to detect hostile aircraft, it needed totally reliable communications over arctic wastes. Bell Laboratories designed the "White Alice" system in which stations up to 200 miles apart were connected by microwaves, a system made possible by the Laboratories development of "over-the-horizon" microwave transmission.

147

In April 1952, a new era in defense technology dawned as the NIKE Ajax System developed by Bell Laboratories destroyed a drone B-17 in flight above the White Sands, N.M., Proving Ground. The NIKE Ajax missile is seen approaching under the target's wing. Never again would high-flying, high-speed bombers be safe from ground fire.

Company subsidiary, the Sandia Corporation, was organized to manage it. Ever since then, a group of Bell Laboratories (as well as Western Electric) people has taken active part in Sandia, and five of its seven presidents through the years have been Bell Laboratories men. All this work has been carried out under nonprofit, no-fee contracts that have been reviewed every few years.

THE NET FLOW AND BENEFIT

Bell Laboratories has done some research and development work of a fairly broad nature under government sponsorship. Such work has included studies of metals and synthetic quartz crystals, microwave diode research, and development of microwave solid-state devices. And generally, the experience of working on government projects brings with it certain knowledge and skills that otherwise might not be acquired. Indeed, to perform work of the kind sketched in the foregoing pages, yet learn nothing, would hardly be possible. Yet the question may nag at the thoughtful person, "Does this mean that a private organization is gaining some benefit at public expense?"

On this point a comment made by then President Fisk of the Laboratories in 1963 is pertinent. "The basic structure of Bell Laboratories' organization," he said, "was established with the Bell System in mind. As military commitments have been assumed, beginning roughly with World War II, we have maintained an organization designed to provide the closest possible association between these military opportunities and our people doing Bell System work. As a consequence, the results of our research, which with very minor exceptions is supported by Bell System funds, are widely available for use by the military. Certainly the two areas cross-fertilize and assist each other, but I think there can be no doubt that the net flow and benefit is from Bell System research and development work toward the military rather than vice versa."*

The thoughtful person will also no doubt reflect that the same kind of transistor that guides one nation's missile also guides another's. It is not to be gainsaid that the arts of communication in which we take pride have their dark aspect. All that is suggested here is that under national necessities as seen by those in authority, Bell Laboratories has worked in good faith and with much success to meet defense responsibilities. A group of five Laboratories men, joint authors of a book that describes the principles of communications technology, have written the rest in three sentences:

"The means of communication, fascinating though they are, are not important in themselves. The important question concerns the use to which they will be put. Unfortunately, this vital question cannot be answered by technology."†

---

*Statement to the Subcommittee on Science, Research and Development, Committee on Science and Astronautics, House of Representatives, December 11, 1963.

†Thomas H. Crowley, Gerard G. Harris, Stewart E. Miller, John R. Pierce and John P. Runyon, *Modern Communications* (New York, Columbia University Press, 1962).

Bell Laboratories began work on air defense systems during World War II and reached a milestone in October 1974 when the SAFEGUARD Ballistic Missile Defense System at Grand Forks, North Dakota, was turned over to the Army. Shown here is the system's Perimeter Acquisition Radar, a computerized complex that detects and tracks intercontinental ballistic missiles at long range.

149

To insure orderly introduction of new systems, inter-
company committees with representatives from Bell
Laboratories, Western Electric and AT&T have been
established. Here, the group that coordinates development
of long-distance communications meets at Holmdel, N.J.

MANAGEMENT STYLES AND DECISIONS 11

Even practical jokes at Bell Laboratories have technical overtones. These two, for example, depend on careful measurement:

Years ago a scientist who proudly wore a new bowler to and from his laboratory was puzzled to distraction when, on successive days, his hat seemed first too small, then too large, then comfortable again, but unaccountably tight a day later. It took him weeks, it is said, to realize that someone had purchased two more hats identical except for size and was making arrhythmic substitutions in the wardrobe.

Another story widely told concerned a member of a group that studies the tastes and habits of telephone users—what people like or dislike in the shape and heft of telephone instruments, how they remember numbers, preferences as to the arrangement of pushbuttons, and a hundred other things. In this instance the man's friends merely snipped a half-inch a day from the cord connecting the handset of his telephone to the base. Eventually he could be seen phoning with his chin almost down on his desk— absorbed in his work and quite unaware that he was serving, so to speak, as his own guinea pig.

But levity has limits at Bell Laboratories. Most of the time this is an extremely serious place, heavily populated by problem-solvers with little time for japery. "The prominent values," Professor Harold Leavitt of Stanford University once commented after considerable observation, "are the values of scientists and technologists everywhere: technical excellence, independence of thought, the expectation that one will be scrutinized by his peers, or rather that his work will be scrutinized."

Leavitt also observed that although nontechnical abilities, such as management skills, are given a secondary place by many, still there is a close consonance between the values of professional employees and the values of the organization; and this, he suggested, has perhaps done much to aid effective management.

Perhaps. Such consonance, however, may also be thought of as a result of management, rather than as an aid. The problems of managing effectively a large organization of people of diverse exceptional gifts— self-motivated and self-demanding, and also inclined to be extremely exacting, critical of others, and alert to any sign of weakness or illogic—these problems are beyond this writer's competence to explore in detail. However, we have already instanced in Chapter 1 some of the main policies, initiatives and tactics characteristic of Bell Laboratories management; and here, looking back across the sweep of 50 years, we can get a general idea of how the leadership has discerned and dealt with changing problems and opportunities.

IN THE BEGINNING . . .

We can start, logically enough, with the initial leadership—a leadership that began in fact long before Bell Laboratories was formally organized. This may be said to have been characterized by an interesting mixture of commercial instinct, careful engineering analysis and romantic enthusiasm.

To explain that, it is useful to go back as far as 1908, when John J. Carty, then chief engineer of AT&T, went to San Francisco to study the telephone situation there. One of the people he took with him was Frank B. Jewett, who at the age of 29 was AT&T's transmission engineer. In San Francisco they found preparations already starting for the Panama-Pacific Exposition, then scheduled for 1914 but later postponed to 1915. They also discovered among Californians an urgent desire for telephone communication with the East.

President Theodore N. Vail of AT&T, coming on the scene a bit later, assured the Exposition management that he would try to have a transcontinental line ready in time for the opening. It was a big promise, true to the Vail tradition. Responsibility for meeting it was placed primarily on young Jewett.

And he met it. It was Jewett who decided, after studious analysis, that the then developing "new physics" would have to be exploited to solve communications problems, and that molecular physicists would have to be employed. It was Jewett who accordingly hired H. D. Arnold, on the advice of Professor Millikan of the University of

Chicago, and so set in motion the work that made transcontinental service a reality in time to fulfill Vail's promise. It was also Jewett who became, at age 37, Western Electric's chief engineer and, nine years later, the first president of Bell Laboratories.

Another man Jewett hired was Oliver E. Buckley, who was later to succeed him as head of the Laboratories. Recalling his own start in the business in 1914, Buckley once wrote, "Industrial research was at that time in its infancy and had little appeal to most of the graduate students in science." He mentioned also that there were only three graduate students then at Cornell, himself included, who were

Frank B. Jewett was Bell Laboratories' first president (1925-1940). Previously he had been chief engineer for Western Electric. Jewett was a pioneer not only in analyzing what had to be done to solve telephone transmission problems, but also in organizing industrial research and development on a large scale.

interested enough to be interviewed when Jewett and a colleague visited Ithaca. However, Jewett succeeded in hiring all of them—a good example of his ability to get things moving. The point is that these were truly pioneering days in industrial research and Jewett had the drive and the touch to get important work into the hands of capable people, many of whom he personally selected. He was, as suggested above, a romantic enthusiast who could get other talented people to work toward goals to which he himself was wholly committed.

Jewett was, some have said, ahead of his time in sensing the opportunities in industrial research. His own words also tell a good deal about him. For instance, a talk he gave in 1929 was entitled "The Romance of Research in the Telephone Industry," and he played the theme to the hilt.

"There is not a single field of that branch of human activity we designate as industry," he said, "which is not replete with elements of romance. . . . In medicine or surgery; in the fever-laden swamps which man desires to use for one purpose or another; in some distant mining camp or remote cannery of the icy north; in the vibrant factory or the quiet countryside traversed by innocent-looking wires on poles or towers, the story is the same if we have but the urge to read what is written. . . ."

Rhetoric, yes. But behind the rhetoric were talents that made Jewett a remarkably successful organizer of technical effort and enabled him to guide Bell Laboratories through the accomplishments of the 1920's and 1930's. Central to his thinking, it is recalled by some who years ago worked under his direction—and central therefore to Bell Laboratories' whole approach to its task—was a firm belief that a group working in concert could accomplish much more than the same people working independently; this on the principle that the interplay of ideas and the intellectual competition on a day-to-day, face-to-face

basis provided a stimulus that no amount of separate effort could equal.

Buckley succeeded Jewett in 1940, as World War II loomed, and it was under Buckley's direction that the Laboratories made the transition to war work. Concerning this, Buckley later made a comment that shows where Laboratories management had put a lot of emphasis during the preceding years.

A SORT OF RELIGION

Two things, he said, made Bell Laboratories unique in its potential ability to contribute to the war effort. One was the attention given to systems engineering— an art, in Buckley's words, "little understood outside of our establishment." Also, he continued, "It is nothing less than a religion of the Laboratories to develop systems and equipment best to serve, rather than best to sell in a competitive market at the sacrifice of quality of performance. These factors are just as essential in military as in telephone system problems and were recognized by the military establishment."

The best-to-serve religion, as Buckley called it, was fundamental in the management stance of his and Jewett's time. No less important, as suggested in Mr. deButts' introduction to this book, had been AT&T's decision to continue research through the depression years of the 1930's. This was essential to the progress that enabled Buckley to recall with pride in 1954, two years after his retirement, that in the postwar period of his administration, "A larger number of important developments were completed than in any other period of that length in Bell Laboratories' history."

SOLID STATESMANSHIP

Looking ahead, however, Buckley foresaw that continuing accomplishment with solid-state electronic devices would dwarf what had gone before; and he suggested that the most important event of his

Oliver E. Buckley, the Laboratories' second president (1940-1951), guided the organization through the critical transition from peacetime to wartime effort; and in the postwar years, it was under Buckley's leadership that Bell Laboratories people introduced new transmission and switching systems and invented the transistor.

administration would prove to have been the work in solid-state physics organized by M. J. Kelly and led by Ralph Bown and J. B. Fisk. In this estimate he was undoubtedly correct. However, Buckley's administration was also the time of some other pivotal management moves. One was the Bell System decision to make Bell Laboratories responsible for quality control of Western Electric production (see page 138). Another was the first step toward

locating Laboratories people at Western Electric factory locations (of which more in a moment). A third was the inception of a wider informational program about Bell Laboratories' work, in addition to long-standing policies of publication in professional and learned journals.

The work in solid-state physics, as Buckley himself noted, was largely sparked by Kelly, who later succeeded him as president. This involved two main decisions. The first was to embark on the program at all. The second, after the still flighty and hard-to-control transistor effect had been discovered, was to proceed with the very large effort required to make truly reliable, useful semiconductor devices. This too was Kelly's doing primarily, but depended on Buckley's and AT&T's agreement and encouragement.

Kelly was a decisive doer, to put it mildly, rather than a give-and-take administrator, and other important courses of action at Bell Laboratories stemmed from his insistence. Two in particular deserve comment.

One was the location of many Laboratories people, as mentioned in Chapter 1, at or near Western Electric manufacturing plants. This has done a great deal to foster close teamwork and easy information-flow between the Laboratories' development and design engineers, on the one hand, and Western Electric production engineers and managers on the other. Today eight Bell Laboratories groups, numbering altogether almost exactly 3000 people, are so located.

This demands management that is alert to maintain close collaboration among Bell Laboratories people of different disciplines notwithstanding geographical separation. And it goes without saying that the various Laboratories groups must not be absorbed by the much larger Western Electric groups with whom they work, but keep their vitality as development-design people and their authority over design and performance standards. No doubt largely because these necessities have been recognized, the hand-in-hand and mind-to-mind teamwork of Western Electric and Bell Laboratories people at manufacturing locations has been indispensable to producing the astonishingly subtle components and systems now required to meet public needs.

Mervin J. Kelly became Bell Laboratories' third president (1951-1959) after years as director of research and later as executive vice president. It was Kelly who, with his associates, largely shaped the program of research on semiconductor materials and later organized fundamental development work to make the transistor reliable.

KELLY COLLEGE

Another aspect of Bell Laboratories life that owes much to Kelly is the strong emphasis on depth of training. Kelly simply demanded this. (When he was in charge of research, as Buckley had been before him and Fisk and Baker were later, and even as executive vice president, he insisted on interviewing many Ph.D. candidates for employment himself.) Bear in mind also that when the semiconductor revolution began, a quarter of a century ago, it was new to the universities and Bell Laboratories people themselves knew more about it than others. So it was that the Laboratories launched a massive in-house educational program that went by the official name of Communications Development Training, or CDT, but was much better known as Kelly College.

Educational programs at Bell Laboratories have changed greatly since then as conditions themselves have changed. The universities, for example, which formerly had no curricula especially pertinent to new developments in communications, now teach the principles behind the transistor—an interesting instance of how Bell Laboratories has influenced all academic education in physics and electrical engineering. But Laboratories management continues to believe that depth of training is vital, requires it, and helps people of promise who do not have it to get it. The technical staff, as it happens, includes the largest group of Ph.D.'s to be found anywhere outside the academe. And the current in-house program of continuing education, which began in 1969, is the largest yet; instructors from within the Laboratories itself (and some also from universities) conduct more than 100 courses each semester attended by nearly 5000 technical employees.

"The goal," says Eugene D. Reed, who for some time served as chairman of the program, "is to prevent technological obsolescence at Bell Laboratories by bringing about a steady state of practice and learning

James B. Fisk, Bell Laboratories' fourth president (1959-1973) like Kelly and Buckley before him had earlier been in charge of research. Under Fisk the Laboratories pioneered satellite communications, developed electronic switching systems, applied solid-state technology to many other uses, and joined with the telephone companies in a common attack on complex operating problems.

covering the entire career span of our technical professionals."

SMALL ARMIES OF EXPERTS

Management problems and styles have continued to change since Kelly's day. The 15 years of Fisk's leadership have seen great growth in the numbers of Bell Laboratories people and the range of their work —a process that almost necessitates a more consultative management. This expansion has paralleled the immense growth of the Bell System in physical facilities, services and customers. Bell Laboratories people are now located at 17 laboratory centers in nine states and the sheer scope of projects like electronic switching calls for small armies of experts.

Other changes, however, have been equally if not more important—and none more so than the deep involvement of Bell Laboratories in ongoing Bell System operations. And this brings up an interesting point.

On the one hand, remarkable successes in solid-state physics, in materials science and computing science, in aspects of behavioral science, and in communications theory, have given the Laboratories exceptional stature in the world of science—something well beyond its standing of years ago. In some fields a year or two of work here is an experience to be prized; and for many people the world over this is a place of pilgrimage.

At the same time, however, the practical necessities of Bell System operations have gripped Bell Laboratories more strongly than ever before. The need (as it is hoped earlier chapters have helped to suggest) is not only to design systems that will improve day-to-day communications performance, but to support the telephone companies in making absolutely sure that all systems will do what they are supposed to do and no mistake.

So the spectrum from theoretical and scientific studies to the practical methodology of operations is broader than ever before. This has been a great part of the management challenge to Fisk and Baker and will surely be no less so to their successors.

A hint of the subtleties involved in managing gifted people in such a time of change may be gained from comments like the following from members of the technical staff.

PERSONAL SATISFACTIONS

"I spent many happy years," said one, "working on fundamental problems I enjoyed. But I still felt the lack of getting involved with what is the essential challenge of Bell Laboratories as I thought it should have been, which is namely the communications business and the application of our ideas as soon as possible into that business. I see that being turned around and this makes me very happy. . . but others I know find the present climate uncomfortable."

Said another, "I was working in reentry physics with people who were doing a really outstanding job. When that ended most of them went into inter-connection technology. There has been a bit of frustration in the time it takes to become involved as expert in a new field. But if the Laboratories can channel the talents these people brought to bear on reentry physics into another field, like interconnection technology, there won't be any place better."

Said the same man also, "I don't think I would go back to working in an academic area that I didn't feel was in the mainstream of the company's business. But there is a drawback too—that you have to give up to some extent the satisfactions of pursuing a specialty to its ultimate refinement. This is a problem that is found everywhere but it is one that Bell Laboratories faces perhaps more than any place else because we have such a concentration of talent. Many people who come here, perhaps most of them, could be at the top of their specialties. The problem

is to utilize the talents, to focus them on projects that are important to the company, and to make the work interesting."

Other comments dwell on the need for communications among people. "It is easy to complain about this," says one executive director, "but the fact is that communication in Bell Laboratories is pretty good. We sit in seminars, we publish, we read, and what-not.

In 1973 William O. Baker, after 18 years as vice president for research, became Bell Laboratories' fifth president. In Baker's view operational complexities are being effectively solved by the melding of communication techniques with computer software; and the development of new systems — including, for example, optical communication systems — will lead to better and more abundant service than ever before.

But most important, we talk and visit. When somebody has a bright idea and thinks it might be useful in somebody else's job, he calls up and explains what he visualizes. When one group tells another it can do something, the commitment can usually be relied on and when a project is stopped, people know the reasons."

Another man, now retired, writes, "During 41 years of work I frequently needed the help of other people with special knowledge. To obtain this it was only necessary to call the specialist and tell him my problem. It made no difference whether we were acquainted or not, or what organization levels we occupied. In 41 years my request was never turned down but was always met with enthusiasm and a breadth of explanation that went far beyond simple courtesy."

On the other hand, one finds another staff member writing apprehensively in *Bell Labs News* about groups in adjacent laboratories who have never met; and he asks, "Will we be consumed by impersonality as a result of working in a large utilitarian organization?" Getting a "no" answer to such a question is recognized as vital to the success of Laboratories management.

SUPPORTING STAFF SERVICES

As Bell Laboratories has grown, in both numbers of people and variety of functions, staff support for the research and development groups has become increasingly important. Ninety years ago the Boston laboratory of the American Bell Telephone Company, predecessor of AT&T, had 29 employees. Among them were four stockmen, three shop workers, a clerk and an office boy. Today, of approximately 17,000 Bell Laboratories people, 7500 are members of the technical staff, 2700 are technical assistants, and 6800 perform the indispensable support services that make it possible for research scientists and development engineers to get on with their jobs. This staff support

entails not only administrative functions and skills. It also includes the design and engineering of buildings, as we have seen in Chapter 1; procurement and installation of equipment; computer systems operation; construction of pilot models and components; equipment design engineering and drafting; testing; preparation of contracts, patent applications and engineering information; and many more essential activities. The structuring of this work has in fact been a major management accomplishment and represents in itself a considerable innovation in the organization of technical effort.

Within the supporting staff organization, too, we find a variety of new approaches, all aimed toward expediting Bell Laboratories' technical effort. Here are several examples, in addition to the trend-setting work in building design:

An environmental health and safety department, organized in 1965, brings together the disciplines of industrial hygiene, toxicology, health physics and radiation protection to aid research scientists and development engineers in evaluating new materials and devices from the safety standpoint. This group is also available to advise all Bell System companies on problems of safety and environmental control and has played a considerable role in helping to formulate national and international standards for the safe use of electromagnetic radiations and control of exotic or unusual chemicals.

Another small staff group has pioneered in the planning and conduct of exchange visits among technical people. Interaction with members of other laboratories is important and can be extremely stimulating to all concerned, but it is a good idea to make sure that the particular people who will really benefit will come together. When visitors come to Bell Laboratories from the other side of the world, for example, the question of who is to see whom needs to be answered in a way that will make the best use of everyone's time. Also, of course, it is necessary to recognize constraints imposed by competition and the need to protect proprietary information. We may note, too, that in recent years other large laboratories, in their conduct of person-to-person technical relations, have been following Bell Laboratories' lead.

The way machine shops have been organized also reflects imaginative staff effort to help get the technical work done effectively. Years ago there was a central model shop. Today at major Bell Laboratories locations there is still a central shop for some kinds of work, but the larger number of mechanics work in small shops close to technical laboratory areas. Thus engineers and mechanics can communicate easily and quickly. Formal drawings are no longer needed and often enough a verbal description is all that a skilled mechanic needs. This saves engineering and drafting time, shortens delivery schedules and reduces costs.

Even budgets and cost accounting are subjects for innovation. Staff people at Bell Laboratories have developed new methods and analytical tools to provide, on demand, any desired combination of data

Financial specialists in the Comptroller's Division continuously improve techniques for managing the Laboratories budget. Most of the Laboratories' support comes from its Bell System owners, AT&T and Western Electric. Bell System telephone companies finance work on business information systems, and defense work is funded by the government.

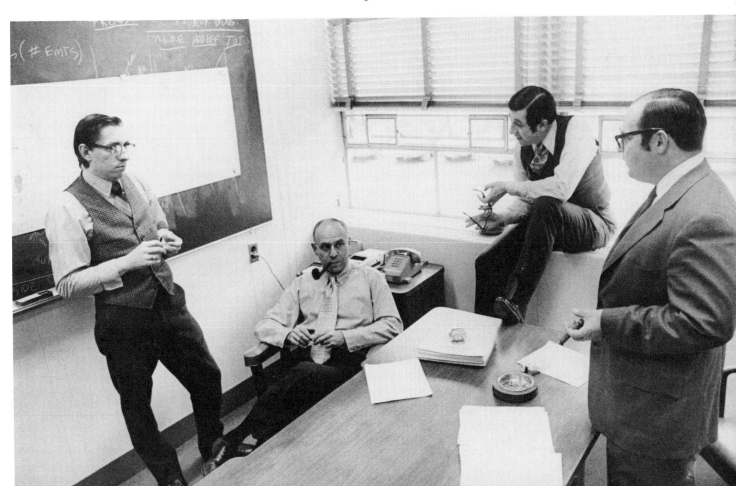

At Bell Laboratories in Denver, patent specialists review an application for a United States patent. Research and development at Bell Laboratories produces discoveries, inventions and innovations that have resulted in an average of about two patents per working day to Laboratories engineers and scientists.

relative to time and the budget. This can be done by organizational unit (of which there are more than 800)—by technical project (there are 5500 of these)—and by particular cost elements such as salaries, materials and services (of which there are more than 150). Thus complete, precise data can be supplied for large projects budgeted in the millions, or for the functioning of a single department that may be at work on a dozen small jobs. Whatever the undertaking, project managers are enabled to keep a steady watch on productiveness in relation to the available money.

One more essential staff service calls for comment. This is the collection, processing and distribution of information that may be needed by Bell scientists

and development engineers wherever they are located. Library and information specialists provide technical reports, bulletins on new developments, translations from foreign technical literature, audiovisual services and a great deal more. Computer and photographic techniques facilitate information storage and retrieval. Bell Laboratories has in fact pioneered in the development and design of library information systems and at present more than 50 informational services use internally generated computer programs for (among other things) automatic indexing, the filtering of desired information from the vast accumulation in the files, and prompt dissemination to the people who need it. As one illustration, a computerized loan system serves five main libraries on a real-time basis (as well as 20 other library locations in an off-line mode), maintains up-to-the-minute accountability for all volumes, pools geographically dispersed resources and follows up requests automatically. This system makes all the libraries equally available and now routinely handles more than 250,000 transactions a year.

NEW INITIATIVES IN A NEW WORLD

A major recent change in the situation of Bell Laboratories—and of the whole Bell System—may be of greater consequence, in its impact on management style, than any yet mentioned. At least so it seems to one observer. This is the ever-increasing pressure of competition.

There are two main reasons why competition in communications has increased rapidly in recent years. One is that the uses and possibilities of electronics (enormously stimulated by Bell Laboratories' transistor discoveries) have simply burgeoned and industry, government and education have all found vast need for the gamut of services the new technology permits. The second reason is that skills in electronics and communications have been diffused all over the world. This is just about the liveliest industry ever

—one may guess, in fact, that no technology has ever had so many enthusiastic practitioners. In the United States alone, more than 500 laboratories are engaged in electronics and communications research and development.

Recalling now Buckley's "religion" of developing equipment that will *serve* best, as contrasted with what may *sell* best in competition, it is clear enough that the most extreme care is needed to make a complicated communication system work dependably. This is as true now as it ever was—in fact even more care is needed today than in the past, as for

Elmer Easton, Chairman of the New Jersey Council for Research and Development, presents the Council's 1972 Outstanding Patent Award to Bell Laboratories switching engineers Dick Jaeger (center) and Amos Joel (right) for the basic Traffic Service Position System (TSPS) patent. Work at the Laboratories has produced more than 17,000 United States patents.

example when digits must flow like lightning without error and a few missed billionths of a second can upset the computer cart.

However, in Jewett's and Buckley's and even in Kelly's time, responsibility to decide what would serve best in the Bell System could be determined in the absence of effective marketplace competition; and there are mountains of evidence that in respect of both quality and cost, equipment and systems developed by Bell Laboratories and made by Western Electric have been markedly superior. Today the situation is fundamentally altered in that competition is far more knowledgeable and aggressive—and as the arts of integrated circuitry proceed and are further diffused, there is little question that competitive skills will continue to increase. It is important also to note that we are speaking here not only of competition in technological know-how, but of competition in imaginative and effective marketing. Furthermore, AT&T and the operating Bell telephone companies have made it unmistakably clear that they will evaluate and choose new equipment and systems wholly on the basis of how well they meet operational, economic and marketing needs, regardless of who designs and produces them.

In short, today's competition requires modern market-ing initiatives at Bell Laboratories. Best-to-serve decisions must be what-will-sell decisions too. The new era of competitive marketing can have no less impact on how Bell Laboratories is managed than on how the telephone companies and Western Electric are to be managed. Today's world of communications, which the Laboratories more than any other organ-ization brought into existence, requires new directions of effort.

One indicator of response was the establishment, a few years ago, of a center at Denver where AT&T, Bell Laboratories and Western Electric people work jointly to plan, design and produce private branch exchange systems. More recently, in 1973, the

At an orientation program for new employees, a Bell Laboratories vice president discusses major goals in his particular area of effort and some of the problems encountered.

Laboratories established what it calls a customer systems engineering center. This President Baker has described to Bell telephone marketing managers as "a prime example of how we are mobilizing our technical talent to meet the market and competitive issues you are identifying as high priorities." It is not hard to detect in this comment a lively awareness that marketing intelligence must flesh out technological understanding and that the practice of purely technical systems engineering is no longer enough.

THE SOURCE OF VITALITY

Looking back over Bell Laboratories' first 50 years, one executive remarked recently that significant changes in emphasis can be discerned, broadly speaking, decade by decade. The first ten years, for instance, were strongly marked by concentration on physical research, advances in electromagnetics, and the establishment of fundamentals for transmission systems. The second decade, which included the war

years, brought new concepts in switching, a remarkable expansion of the radio spectrum into the microwave region and also, perforce, preoccupation with military need, notably in radar (itself a microwave phenomenon), and a temporary recess in work on services for the general public. The next ten years, beginning in late 1945, were the time of the genesis of transistor and related semiconductor devices, while the period from the mid-50's to mid-60's was devoted largely to expansion of the new technology and its exploitation in new systems previously impossible of accomplishment. And most recently, while this same expansion and exploitation of transistor technology has of course continued, Bell Laboratories has joined with the telephone companies to use new resources of analysis in programs aimed at making better use of the whole range of available communications devices and systems.

Any such thumbnail synopsis, of course, leaves out as much as it includes. In different terms, we have seen the Laboratories' task, in Jewett's eyes, as pioneering adventure; we have seen it in Buckley's view as carrying out a religious responsibility for service quality; we have seen it as the building of a new technology from new science, under Kelly's driving direction; and as reaching from subatomic studies to the tough imperatives of day-to-day telephone operations in the world of Fisk and Baker.

Those are not meant as descriptions to be entirely separated. Something of each is in them all. Yet management styles have been widely different and stresses have changed and changed again. What, then, gives Bell Laboratories its essential character and vitality?

The answer is simple. Bell Laboratories is part of the Bell System. This is *the* prime fact about all its work.

The Bell System had goals, and faced problems, that demanded continuous scientific and engineering effort of the highest caliber. It had needs that drew new knowledge out of earth and air and space and from the study of man himself. It had a structure that could absorb and use this knowledge and put it to work for people.

How many Bell Laboratories discoveries and developments would have been made if there had been no Bell System of which the Laboratories could be a part? It is inconceivable that the depth and range of achievement could have been as great. For what equally productive organization could have functioned somewhere off in limbo, busily creating—what? Every creative institution needs clearly defined purposes. Those of Bell Laboratories have been compelling.

Mathematician R. W. Hamming conducts a course in numerical analysis offered to Bell Laboratories staff members through a broad continuing education program. Here, Hamming's lecture is being videotaped for use at other Laboratories locations.

Two Bell Laboratories scientists participate in the search for ways to recover and reuse plastic compounds the Bell System uses for cable and wire insulation, telephone housings and many other purposes. Plastic, once regarded as scrap after equipment was taken out of service, is being recycled as a scarce material along with copper and other substances.

AN APPRAISAL

12

Most of the major technical advances in telephony and in data communications have been along lines marked out and developed by the people of Bell Laboratories and its predecessor organizations.

It is Bell scientists and engineers who have made it possible for anyone to talk with anyone else, anywhere, anytime. To do this they have conceived and designed cable and radio systems that span continents and oceans, made these systems capable of carrying more and more information, and developed facilities and methods that give everyone connected to the universal communications network the power of infinite selectivity, usually in a matter of seconds.

Enterprise at Bell Laboratories has produced continuously more efficient and versatile systems and instrumentalities. Transmitting, amplifying, receiving and control systems of increasing talent and reliability; ocean cables, coaxial systems, helical waveguides; and now, coming soon, optical communication systems. Systems employing long radio waves, short waves, centimeter waves, millimeter waves, waves of visible light and waves of infrared.

Transmission structures designed and redesigned, better insulated, better sheathed, water-resistant, more and more of them underground and out of sight. Switching systems that have evolved from jacks, plugs and flexible cords to electronic machines storing, many of them, more complex programs than any computers on earth.

From the same sources have come basic concepts and principles underlying modern communications: noise theory, network theory, modulation theory, information theory, the principle of negative feedback. Automatic alternate routing and "protection" switching from channel to channel. A nationwide hierarchy of major and tributary switching centers under common control. Error-detecting and error-correcting codes for data communications. The concept and practice of systems engineering. "Self-auditing" arrangements for maintaining constant surveillance over complex working systems.

Bell scientists and engineers gave pictures wings; laid the foundations for network radio and television broadcasting, sound motion pictures and high-fidelity recording; built and put "on line" the first high-speed electrical calculators; made possible the transmission of business-machine data between any points on the communications network. They generated the semiconductor revolution and led industry into the age of solid-state electronics. Their discoveries and developments in magnetic alloys, polymers, insulators, ceramics, thin films—purification of crystals, control of additives, "molecular engineering"—constitute an unmatched contribution to the science of materials and are applied in industries around the world.

Bell Laboratories has been an important national resource in defense. Its scientific and systems engineering skills have been indispensable to astronautics and to the exploration and use of space. Through cross-licensing agreements under the patent system, other companies have had ready access to thousands of Bell inventions through the years.

In the Spring, 1973 issue of *Daedalus,* journal of the American Academy of Arts and Sciences, Dean Harvey Brooks of the Harvard Engineering School discussed problems of science policy in the 1970's. Commenting on the organization of research and development at Bell Laboratories, he wrote, "The Bell System represents the best example of a highly integrated technical structure in a high-technology industry and is widely regarded as the most successful and innovative technical organization in the world."

In the same issue of *Daedalus* Professor Charles H. Townes of the University of California looked at some of the economics of Bell Laboratories work. It was Townes whose studies years ago as a Laboratories staff member, and later as a consultant to the Laboratories, led to his concepts of the maser and laser.

Townes noted that the cost of Bell System support of Bell Laboratories, from the mid-1920's to 1965,

Studying synthetic crystal growth under the guidance of a Bell Laboratories chemist, a junior high school student gets first-hand scientific experience during a summer science program held each year at several Laboratories locations. The program is one of several projects run by the Laboratories for minority groups.

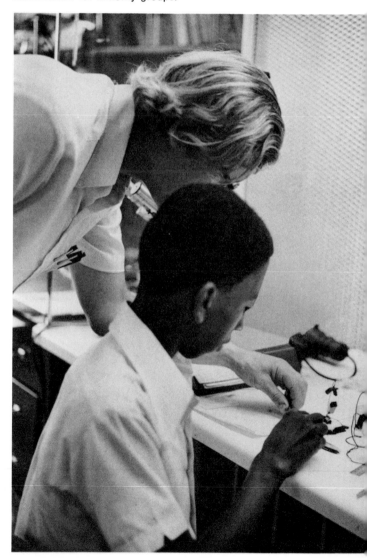

was somewhat less than $2 billion. He also suggested that the cost of long-distance telephony to American society in 1965, which he placed at about $4 billion, was probably not more than a twelfth of what it would have been if the methods and prices of 30 years earlier had remained in effect. "Thus," he concluded, "the decrease in cost of service each year is much larger than the total monetary support of Bell Laboratories over their entire history, and these contributions to long-distance telephony are, of course, only a part of the Laboratories' work."

Also in 1973, Dr. Philip H. Abelson, president of the Carnegie Institution of Washington and editor of *Science,* addressing the International Meeting on the Organization of Science, held in Madrid, said, "As editor of *Science,* I have found the Bell Laboratories to be the best industrial source of scientific articles." And in the context of economic performance Abelson too, like Townes, concluded that annual savings in the cost of long distance were at least equivalent to the total cost of running Bell Laboratories since it was organized in 1925.

Such calculations are surely not intended to be taken literally, for at twelve times the cost, use of the service would be a small fraction of what it is in actuality. However, they do suggest in a dramatic way how effectively research and development have pulled down cost barriers to usage.

Electrical communication will never be free. The overall costs of telephony have been restrained, however, much more successfully than those of most other goods and services, including food, clothing, shelter and transportation. While many factors of operation and management have been essential to these results, the central factor has been the technology and the central factor in the technology has been Bell Laboratories.

The previous chapter suggested that the vitality of Bell Laboratories flows from the charge placed upon

Bell Laboratories scientists Lloyd B. Kreuzer (left) and C. Kumar N. Patel collect a sample of automobile exhaust. Toxic gases in the sample can then be measured quickly and accurately, using a laser technique developed at the Laboratories for measuring air pollution. This is one example of a number of research projects in which Laboratories scientists are studying environmental pollution and its impact.

it by reason of its being part of the Bell System. Discoveries lead to services, and operating and engineering problems stimulate effort to discover. We now conclude with the equally simple, and perhaps self-evident, thought that the telephone companies depend on Bell Laboratories for results as much as the latter depends on them for inspiration —and the more so today because what President Baker calls operational technology requires no lesser technical skills than are needed to develop new technologies. In fact, a Bell System without a Bell Laboratories—a high-technology business without its high-technology core—is hard to imagine.

By voice and gesture, a Bell Laboratories employee leads a class in English for foreign-born residents of Morris County, N.J. Now in its eighth year, the program is one of a wide range of community-action projects to which Laboratories people contribute time and talent after work.

These four students are studying at Columbia University as part of a Bell Laboratories program that encourages members of minority groups to become engineers. With the aid of scholarships, students in the program attend Columbia and various engineering schools full time and work in Laboratories technical departments during the summer. After graduation, they become eligible for employment at Bell Laboratories.

To keep the Bell System informed about its work, Bell Laboratories sponsors group visits, disseminates news stories, oversees publication of technical books and articles, and prepares booklets, films, exhibits and other information for wide distribution. Here, the editorial staff *Bell Laboratories Record* prepares material for the magazine, designed primarily for engineers and managers in the telephone companies.

Members of the Bell Laboratories library staff at Murray Hill, N.J., work at the check-out desk on a balcony above the visitors' reception area. The Murray Hill branch of the library network contains 20,000 books, 35,000 bound technical and professional journals, and copies of more than 1300 other journals and magazines. The library has been a leader in using computer-aided systems for information storage and retrieval.

But is it really? Do not other communications companies, and government telephone and telegraph administrations, get along in different fashion? And would not competitive development engineering serve as well? Or perhaps better?

Those are several different questions. The answers need not take us long. Looking to the past, if this book has said anything, it has said that leadership in communications has been achieved by a Bell System *with* a Bell Laboratories. With respect to government communications administrations (omitting any comment about quality of service except that this varies considerably from country to country) the trend is rather more toward integrating research and development with manufacture and operations than otherwise. In their variety, government administrations have demonstrated that non-integration of R&D with both manufacturing and operating is associated with slowness to innovate and inadequate service, and that functional integration of these three aspects leads to more rapid innovation, better service, lower relative costs and new services.

Looking at the present and future in the United States, where competitive skills in electronics now abound, there can be no doubt that Bell Laboratories must prove itself today in a world quite different from that of 50 years ago, when it was formed. However, the intrinsic value of having a competent research and development organization at the heart of the operating complex, in close and constant touch with all its problems and opportunities, seems plain. The rightness of the positioning increases the challenge to performance.

Appendix I SOME NOTABLE ACHIEVEMENTS BY BELL LABORATORIES PEOPLE

For 50 years, Bell Laboratories' mission has been to do the basic research, development and design, and systems engineering necessary to provide the Bell System with new and improved equipment and services for communications. In working toward this goal, Bell Laboratories people over the years have had a wide impact on Bell System operations as well as in fields other than communications. The names and accomplishments of a few of these people appear in this book. They are only some of the tens of thousands whose efforts and accomplishments have played a part in the story of Bell Laboratories science and engineering.

ORIGINATION OF SOUND MOTION PICTURES

The first sound motion picture with synchronized musical score—"Don Juan" (1926)—was made with audio equipment developed by Bell Laboratories. One year later, "The Jazz Singer," the first film with synchronized dialogue, was made using techniques also developed by the Laboratories.

DEMONSTRATION OF FIRST HIGH-FIDELITY SOUND RECORDING

A long series of Bell System innovations led to the first electric recording system that could be called "hi-fi" and, in 1925, to the Orthophonic phonograph, licensed to the Victor Talking Machine Co. under Western Electric patents. Then, in 1933, the Bell System demonstrated the transmission of stereophonic sound.

DEVELOPMENT OF RADIO ALTIMETER

The radio altimeter, developed by Bell Laboratories in 1939, shows pilots how high above the ground their aircraft is by bouncing FM radio signals off the surface of the earth and using a broadband receiver to track the reflections. This principle is used universally in radio altimeters today.

DEVELOPMENT OF ARTIFICIAL LARYNX

In 1929, a reed-type artificial larynx was developed at Bell Laboratories that enabled thousands of people who had lost their voices through disease or accident to regain the power of speech. In 1960, an improved transistorized instrument was introduced.

ORIGINATION OF RADIO ASTRONOMY

While looking for the sources of static in overseas radio signals, K. G. Jansky in 1933 discovered radio energy coming from the stars—thus launching the science of radio astronomy.

DISCOVERY OF WAVE NATURE OF MATTER

The idea that matter could in some circumstances behave like waves was demonstrated in an experiment at Bell Laboratories in 1927, in which electrons diffracted from a nickel surface showed wave-like behavior. For this work C. J. Davisson shared the 1937 Nobel Prize in Physics.

CREATION OF INFORMATION THEORY

C. E. Shannon's now-classic papers on information theory, published in 1948, quantified "information" and gave engineers a mathematics-based benchmark

—a theoretical maximum information-carrying capacity for any communications system.

DEVELOPMENT OF SOUND SPECTROGRAPH

In the early 1940's, R. K. Potter and his associates at Bell Laboratories developed the sound spectrograph, a device that presents the structure of speech visually for quantitative measurement. It is widely used by hospitals, universities and industry.

SCIENTIFIC APPROACH TO QUALITY CONTROL

Over 40 years ago, W. A. Shewhart founded statistical quality control—combining mathematics, engineering and economics to assure that Bell System equipment would perform as expected.

RESEARCH ON SUPERCONDUCTIVITY

Work by Laboratories scientists B. T. Matthias, T. H. Geballe, J. E. Kunzler, L. R. Testardi and their associates has resulted in the discovery of hundreds of superconducting materials that lose all resistance to the flow of electricity at low temperatures; the first "supermagnets" (small devices that produce high-intensity magnetic fields formerly requiring much larger electromagnets); and significant increases in the highest temperature at which a material remains superconducting. Some of the most important superconductors—including niobium-tin, niobium-zirconium, niobium-germanium, niobium-titanium— were among the many discovered at Bell Laboratories.

LASER INVENTIONS

The laser was invented in 1958 by Bell Laboratories scientist Arthur Schawlow and C. H. Townes, a consultant to the Laboratories. In 1960, Ali Javan, W. R. Bennett, Jr., and D. R. Herriott of the Laboratories—using a mixture of helium and neon— demonstrated the first continuously operating gas laser. Later C. K. N. Patel conceived and developed the first carbon dioxide laser, the most powerful continuously operating laser now available.

APPLICATION OF SYSTEMS ENGINEERING CONCEPT

In the 1930's, Bell Laboratories refined and applied the concept of systems engineering, an organized approach to decision-making first conceived and applied in the Bell System well before the 1920's. With this concept, now widely used in industry, a proposed innovation is evaluated in terms of technical feasibility, compatibility with existing and future systems, possible alternative solutions, economic feasibility and other criteria before being acted upon.

DEVELOPMENT OF THE AUDIOMETER

In the 1920's, Harvey Fletcher, R. L. Wegel and others at Bell Laboratories established the scientific basis for measuring human hearing. Their work produced internationally accepted loudness standards, audiometers for testing human hearing, and procedures for analyzing and compensating for hearing impairments.

INVENTION OF THE VOCODER

In 1936, Bell Laboratories developed the voice coder, or vocoder, for analyzing the pitch and energy content of speech waves. With later developments, vocoder output was digitized, encrypted and the digital signal transmitted within a voice channel. The vocoder has been used since World War II by the U.S. Government for secure communications.

DISCOVERY OF THERMAL NOISE

In 1926, Bell Laboratories scientist J. B. Johnson discovered and measured thermal noise, a phenomenon of materials that sets limits on their ability to amplify electric currents. This fundamental discovery cleared the way for more effective design of amplifiers, not only for telephone systems but also for all other sensitive electronic systems.

INVENTION OF NEGATIVE FEEDBACK AMPLIFIER

In one of the most fundamental discoveries in the history of communications, H. S. Black in 1927 at

Bell Laboratories found that by feeding part of an amplifier's output back into its input (negative feedback), it was possible by sacrificing some amplification to achieve stable operation at low distortion. More recently an early idea of Black's for an error-cancelling scheme (feedforward) was rediscovered by Harold Seidel and his associates at the Laboratories and found to be useful for applications involving very large bandwidths.

DEVELOPMENT OF QUARTZ CRYSTAL FILTERS

In the late 1920's, Bell Laboratories engineers created a body of knowledge and techniques for designing and manufacturing quartz filters—highly selective electrical networks—for use in practically every type of modern communications system. In the early 1950's, A. C. Walker, Ernest Buehler and G. J. Kohman of the Laboratories demonstrated the feasibility of producing synthetic quartz. This work was extended by R. A. Laudise of the Laboratories and R. A. Sullivan of the Western Electric Co., so that by the early 1960's Western Electric was supplying most of Bell System needs for quartz with synthetic material, thus rendering the U.S. independent of uncertain foreign sources.

INVENTION OF THE TRANSISTOR

The transistor was invented at Bell Laboratories in 1947 by John Bardeen, Walter Brattain and William Shockley. For their work they received the 1956 Nobel Prize in Physics. All of today's integrated circuits embody the basic concepts and technology of this invention.

INVENTION OF THE SOLAR BATTERY

As an outgrowth of work on transistors, Bell Laboratories scientists D. M. Chapin, C. S. Fuller and G. L. Pearson in 1954 invented the silicon solar battery—an efficient device for converting sunlight directly into electricity. Arrays of these devices are used to power satellites and as energy sources for other uses.

DEVELOPMENT OF ZONE REFINING TECHNIQUES

Beginning about 1951, Bell Laboratories' W. G. Pfann and associates developed ways of passing molten zones through solid semiconductors to sweep them free of impurities—a critical step in making crystals of transistor quality.

INVENTION OF FIELD-EFFECT TRANSISTOR

The first practical field-effect transistor was invented by William Shockley at Bell Laboratories in 1951. The most important commercial form in use today, the IGFET, was developed by M. M. Atalla and Dawon Kahng of the Laboratories in 1959.

DEVELOPMENT OF OXIDE MASKING

In 1954, Lincoln Derick and C. J. Frosch of Bell Laboratories developed the process of oxide masking, now widely used to make integrated circuits from silicon crystals. Oxidized silicon forms a barrier, or mask, against "dopants" (additional elements) diffused into the crystals through etched holes in the oxide to achieve desired electrical properties.

INVENTION OF EPITAXIAL TRANSISTOR

Today, essentially all high-speed transistors, and many incorporated into integrated circuits, are "epitaxial" transistors of the kind invented in 1960 at Bell Laboratories. The devices are named for a major process in their fabrication. By growing the transistor material in thin "epitaxial" layers—layers having the same crystalline structure as the wafer on which they are grown—J. J. Kleimack, H. H. Loar, I. M. Ross and H. C. Theuerer made possible high-quality, low-cost transistors and provided a process later important for making integrated circuits.

RESEARCH ON SYNTHETIC GARNETS

Since the late 50's, research at Bell Laboratories by L. G. Van Uitert has resulted in the synthesis of valuable new garnet materials and techniques for growing these crystals free of defects to a useful size and configuration. These achievements have been important to such Laboratories developments as magnetic bubble devices, solid-state lasers and devices for microwave and optical transmission systems.

INVENTION OF THE "IMPATT" DIODE

In 1964, Bell Laboratories scientists R. L. Johnston and B. C. DeLoach discovered the IMPATT (IMPact Avalanche Transit Time) diode, subsequently shown to operate by an effect proposed earlier by W. T. Read, Jr., also of the Laboratories. IMPATT diodes—semiconductor devices that generate microwaves directly when a DC voltage is applied to them—are becoming increasingly important in the design of microwave systems because of their high reliability and low cost, and are being used in the experimental millimeter waveguide system currently under test.

INVENTION OF CHARGE-COUPLED DEVICES (CCD's)

In 1970, W. S. Boyle and G. E. Smith, both of Bell Laboratories, invented CCD's, which can potentially replace highly complex integrated circuits in imaging, logic and memory applications. CCD's operate by manipulating small packets of electrical charge in a slice of semiconductor.

INVENTION OF MAGNETIC BUBBLE DEVICES

In 1966, A. H. Bobeck and others at Bell Laboratories invented magnetic bubble technology, which can provide a solid-state replacement for large-capacity memories. Data are stored in minute bubble-like magnetic domains in a thin film of magnetic material.

CONTRIBUTIONS TO LIGHT-EMITTING DIODE TECHNOLOGY

Bell Laboratories research studies of certain semiconductor compounds by D. G. Thomas, J. J. Hopfield, C. J. Frosch and others at the Laboratories led to the discovery of the basic physical process by which light is created in gallium phosphide light-emitting diodes (LED's). LED's are now finding many communications uses where their colors, high reliability and low power consumption make them preferable to tungsten lamps.

CREATION OF LITHIUM-TANTALATE CRYSTALS

Man-made lithium-tantalate crystals grown initially at Bell Laboratories are the first practical alternative to quartz for converting mechanical energy into electrical energy in communication system filters. Such filters have potential for high-capacity transmission systems.

DEVELOPMENT OF CLOSE-SPACED TRIODE

In 1944, J. A. Morton conceived and developed a new type of vacuum tube based on electrode spacing narrower than a human hair. The reliable high-frequency performance of this "close-spaced triode" made transcontinental television possible; it is also extensively used for long-distance telephone transmission.

DISCOVERY OF THERMO-COMPRESSION BONDING

In the 1950's, O. L. Anderson, Howard Christensen and Peter Andreatch of Bell Laboratories discovered a new bonding technique particularly useful for connecting transistors to other elements in electronic circuits. The technique, pressing the connecting wire to the transistor mounting at low heat levels, provides a firm bond without introducing undesired electrical properties and has been widely used throughout the electronics industry. It is particularly advantageous in avoiding contamination, thus achieving long life and reliability.

DEVELOPMENT OF THE MAGNETRON

Early in World War II, studies by J. B. Fisk, H. D. Hagstrum and others at Bell Laboratories made it practical to generate high-power microwaves by magnetrons, vacuum tubes that capitalize on the motion of electrons in strong magnetic fields to generate high-power microwave frequencies. Magnetrons made microwave radars available to the allies and had an important influence on the outcome of the war. More recently, microwave ovens and other industrial equipment have used high-power magnetrons.

DEVELOPMENT OF KLYSTRONS

Innovative understanding of these prime sources of microwave energy early in World War II led to their becoming essential elements of all military microwave radars. J. R. Pierce, W. G. Shepherd and their associates designed nine of the ten receiving klystrons on the Army-Navy preferred list in 1945. Later commercial communication and test equipment used these "velocity variation" electron tubes extensively.

DEVELOPMENT OF THERMISTORS

Thermistors (a contraction for *therm*al res*istors*) are semiconductor devices whose electrical resistance changes rapidly with changes in temperature. About 1940, G. L. Pearson and his associates at Bell Laboratories developed materials that allowed manufacture of stable, long-life thermistors. They are used for temperature measurement and temperature compensation in automobiles and aircraft, for communications circuitry, in meteorology and in equipment for controlling flow rates.

DEVELOPMENT OF PARAMETRIC AMPLIFIERS

A wide variety of solid-state devices called parametric amplifiers or variable-reactance amplifiers were developed by Bell Laboratories scientists during the 1950's. Because they have a low noise level that approaches the minimum noise levels found in intergalactic space, parametric amplifiers are used in ground stations of satellite communication systems, in radio astronomy and as laboratory tools for detecting very weak radiation.

DEVELOPMENT OF SOLDERLESS-WRAPPED CONNECTIONS

In 1953, Bell Laboratories engineers demonstrated that wires can be electrically connected in half the usual time but with full conductivity and reliability— without solder. A specially developed tool is used to wrap the wire tightly around a terminal.

INTRODUCTION OF POLYETHYLENE CABLE SHEATH AND WIRE INSULATION

Bell Laboratories scientists began research on polyethylene in 1940 and by 1947 had introduced the first polyethylene cable sheath to replace those made of lead. The Laboratories also designed polyethylene insulation for cables and telephone wires.

FIRST LONG-DISTANCE TV TRANSMISSION

In 1927, following Bell Laboratories fundamental studies of vision and the conversion of light to electrical current, the Bell System publicly demonstrated the first long-distance transmission of live television over wires. This pioneering work helped establish the technical basis for the first commercial service ten years later.

CONTRIBUTIONS TO COMMUNICATIONS NETWORK THEORY

Bell Laboratories people H. W. Bode, Sidney Darlington, Harry Nyquist, S. O. Rice and others have made fundamental discoveries in feedback theory, stability criteria, network synthesis and noise theory. Such work has led to greatly improved transmission quality and efficiency in communications systems.

CONTRIBUTIONS TO TRANSMISSION

Bell Laboratories' many contributions to improving transmission systems include new ways of multiplexing (sending more than one telephone call or other signal per circuit), better codes for digital transmission, "pulse stuffing" (adding pulses as a way of synchronizing digital systems) and the invention of companding (compressing a signal's dynamic range at the sending terminal and expanding it at the receiver in order to obtain a better signal-to-noise ratio).

FORMULATION OF ANTENNA THEORY

Long a leader in studies of the propagation of radio waves, Bell Laboratories has as part of this work made important contributions to the theory of radio antennas. Results have included Edmond Bruce's and H. T. Friis' rhombic antenna, which made possible the rapid development of overseas radiotelephone communications in the 1930's, the MUSA (Multiple Unit Steerable Antenna) system, the horn-reflector antenna widely used in commercial microwave systems, and antennas used for "over-the-horizon" microwave propagation.

INVENTION OF AUTOMATIC EQUALIZER

Important circuits called equalizers reshape distorted signals during transmission. In 1964, R. W. Lucky and associates at Bell Laboratories devised an equalizer that automatically adapts to a transmission line's changing electrical characteristics, thus greatly improving data performance. Such automatic-adaptive equalizers are now built into most modern high-speed data sets.

DEVELOPMENT OF COAXIAL CABLE CARRIER SYSTEM

To overcome the bandwidth and distance limitations of ordinary pairs of wires, Lloyd Espenschied and H. A. Affel in 1929 developed the coaxial cable system—a way of sending many telephone calls or other communications signals over coaxial lines.

DEVELOPMENT OF IMPROVED TRAVELING-WAVE TUBE

In 1944, J. R. Pierce of Bell Laboratories achieved stable amplification in the traveling-wave tube—a device invented earlier by Rudolf Kompfner before he joined the Laboratories. The improved tube, which is able to amplify the widest range of microwave frequencies with the highest power achieved to date, is employed in long-distance telephony, satellite communications, defense and space guidance systems, and precision laboratory equipment.

DEVELOPMENT OF MICROWAVE TECHNOLOGY

Bell Laboratories innovations in microwave equipment include waveguides, antennas, power sources and other devices. Many of these resulted from Laboratories' pioneering work on microwave theory and waveguide propagation, including tests at microwave frequencies beginning in 1938. This work greatly aided World War II radar and later resulted in the first commercial microwave radio line, which opened in 1948. Today microwave communications crisscross the nation.

DEVELOPMENT OF TRANSATLANTIC TELEPHONE CABLE SYSTEM

To send telephone calls under the ocean, ways had to be found to put electronic amplifiers on the bottom, power them, and make them reliable enough to operate for many years. After a successful trial with such a system to Cuba, the first cable to Europe was layed in 1956.

DEVELOPMENT OF TELSTAR COMMUNICATIONS SATELLITES

After bouncing coast-to-coast telephone calls off the Echo balloon, Bell Laboratories scientists and engineers developed the Telstar satellites, and demonstrated the feasibility of long-distance telecommunications via an orbiting satellite in 1962 (Telstar I) and 1963 (Telstar II). This project was funded in its entirety by the Bell System.

DEVELOPMENT OF DIGITAL TRANSMISSION SYSTEMS

After pioneering research and development by Bell Laboratories, the Bell System introduced the first commercial "Pulse-Code Modulation" (PCM) system in 1962, the T1 system. Using PCM or similar codes to convert analog—or continuous—signals to digital form, systems of this type now carry as many as 96 phone calls over a single pair of wires.

DEVELOPMENT OF ELECTRONIC SYSTEMS FOR THE LOOP PLANT

In recent years, Bell Laboratories engineers have completed several electronic developments aimed at improving rural telephone service: an inexpensive amplifier (Range Extender with Gain) that expands central office serving areas and two digital transmission systems (Subscriber Loop Multiplexer and Subscriber Loop Carrier) that use only two pairs of wires to bring single-party service to 80 and 40 rural customers, respectively.

DEVELOPMENT OF THE WAVEGUIDE TRANSMISSION SYSTEM

Beginning in 1931, S. A. Schelkunoff, G. C. Southworth and others discovered and experimented with ways of sending communication signals down hollow tube-like structures. Inherently capable of handling huge amounts of communications, such a system, employing precisely made steel and copper tubes, is under development at Bell Laboratories.

DEVELOPMENT OF TASI

Time Assignment Speech Interpolation (TASI) is a high-speed switching and transmission technique that uses listening time and other natural pauses in one speaker's conversation to transmit portions of other conversations. Developed in 1959, TASI substantially increases the telephone circuit capacity of communication channels such as submarine cable systems.

DEVELOPMENT OF RADIOTELEPHONY

In 1926, the first two-way radiotelephone conversation across the Atlantic Ocean took place. Commercial radiotelephone service for aircraft, ships and land vehicles was introduced subsequently but the number of customers for these services has been limited by the availability of radio channels. In 1974, when additional channels became available, Bell Laboratories proposed a high-capacity mobile radiotelephone system that capitalized on multiple use of frequencies and the flexibility of electronic switching to serve large numbers of subscribers at lower cost than with earlier systems.

DEVELOPMENT OF COMMON CONTROL CROSSBAR SWITCHING

Beginning in the late 1930's, Bell Laboratories engineers developed crossbar switching systems, the most versatile telephone switching systems designed prior to electronic switching. These systems include an advanced type of common control in which the cost and complexity of the control equipment are offset by the fact that it can be shared by all lines of the central office and used only briefly to handle each call.

ORIGINATION OF DIRECT DISTANCE DIALING SERVICE

In 1951, as a first step in a program for direct dialing of virtually all long-distance calls, Bell Laboratories helped conduct a field trial in which customers in Englewood, N. J., began dialing directly to selected areas across the nation. During the following years, the Bell System rapidly provided this service to almost all of its customers.

DEVELOPMENT OF ELECTRONIC SWITCHING SYSTEMS

In 1960, Bell Laboratories field tested the first of a family of Bell System electronic switching systems, which use the speed and versatility of electronics technology. In these systems, services can be modified or new ones created by electronically altering the system's "memories"—without rewiring or replacing equipment.

DEVELOPMENT OF WIRE-SPRING RELAY

A relay developed at Bell Laboratories in the late 1940's is still used extensively in the control circuits of modern electromechanical telephone switching systems. Compared to the older types, the wire-spring relay has fewer parts, is easier to manufacture, lasts longer, operates faster and requires half the power.

INVENTION OF FERREED SWITCH

The ferreed switch, invented at Bell Laboratories in the late 1950's, comprises two or four sealed-in-glass contacts and is controlled by magnetized wire coils. Ferreed switches, used to switch phone calls in most electronic switching systems, are smaller, faster operating and require less power than older switching devices.

DEVELOPMENT OF STORE-AND-FORWARD SWITCHING SYSTEMS

An efficient, speedy system for switching teletypewriter messages was devised at Bell Laboratories by W. M. Bacon around 1938. Later known as store-and-forward switching, it replaced earlier manual procedures for switching, storing and routing the volume of teletypewriter traffic generated by organizations with widely separated offices.

DEVELOPMENT OF MULTIFREQUENCY SIGNALING

In the early 1940's, Bell Laboratories developed operator equipment that used tones instead of dial pulses as signals for setting up toll calls through the telephone network.

DEVELOPMENT OF PICTUREPHONE SYSTEM

Picturephone service added a new, visual dimension to telecommunications. First introduced in 1970, the system allows users to see as well as talk to each other and serves as a terminal for viewing such things as computer-stored information, X rays, pages of text, or photographs. Development of the system is continuing with work being done on additional applications for visual communications.

DEVELOPMENT OF TOUCH-TONE TELEPHONE

In 1964, the first Touch-Tone telephone sets went into service. These sets use buttons instead of rotary dials for placing phone calls—an innovation that improves dialing speed. Calls are connected through the telephone network by means of various tones the sets generate, instead of by dial pulses.

DEVELOPMENT OF DATAPHONE SETS

Bell Laboratories people pioneered in transmitting digital data over the voice network and, beginning in the 1960's, developed about 100 distinct types of Dataphone sets. These sets convert digital data to analog signals for transmission over the voice network and reconvert received analog signals back to digital data. Since the original line of sets, modern technology has led to a new family of data sets with greatly improved features and performance.

INVENTION OF THE ELECTRICAL DIGITAL COMPUTER

In 1937, Ball Laboratories mathematician G. R. Stibitz applied telephone switching technology to design a relay digital computer. With this computer, the Laboratories scientist demonstrated the first use of a remote computer terminal and data link in 1940.

DEVELOPMENT OF 500-TYPE TELEPHONE

In 1949, the Bell System introduced the first commercial version of the 500-type telephone. The set, developed by Bell Laboratories for homes and businesses, has a rugged design, improved electronics and an adjustable volume control for the ringer. Now offered in several colors and with Touch-Tone dialing, it has become the most widely used telephone in the United States.

CONCEPTION OF THE ELECTRONIC ANALOG COMPUTER

In 1940, D. B. Parkinson and C. A. Lovell first conceived the fundamental idea for electronic analog computers. The first application was controlling World War II antiaircraft guns in the M9 gun director. This unit was credited with knocking down 76 per cent of the German buzz bombs flying through the sectors it defended in England.

ORIGINATION OF ERROR-CORRECTING CODES

In the late 1940's, R. W. Hamming and others at Bell Laboratories devised error-correcting and error-detecting codes which permit data to be stored,

retrieved and transmitted error-free. Hamming codes are now routinely used in the computer industry.

DEVELOPMENT OF COMPUTER OPERATING SYSTEMS

In addition to hardware, a computer needs an essential piece of software—its operating system. Beginning in the mid-1950's, V. M. Wolontis and R. W. Hamming pioneered with operating systems designed to make the early large computers easy to use—an effort that has continued through numerous Bell Laboratories systems including UNIX, a modern time-shared operating system for minicomputers.

DEVELOPMENT OF COMPUTER GRAPHIC TECHNIQUES

Using innovative computer programs and remote terminals, Bell Laboratories researchers including K. C. Knowlton and E. E. Zajac in the 1960's devised new ways of using the computer's power to store, manipulate and present information. For example, computers display data in various graphic forms, analyze multiple variables and display the results, simulate operation of circuits and design new circuits.

DEVELOPMENT OF REAL-TIME DIGITAL PROCESSORS

In the mid-1960's, Bell Laboratories engineers combined a mathematical procedure known as the "Fast Fourier Transform" and a special digital computer to process complex waveforms in "real time" (or as fast as they are received), making possible fast, economical analysis and filtering of complicated communications signals.

DEVELOPMENT OF CENTRALIZED MAINTENANCE SYSTEMS

Since the 1960's, Bell Laboratories has been developing a wide variety of modern computer-aided techniques to monitor performance of switching and transmission equipment. Aided by these systems, telephone companies can detect and locate network problems for quick repair.

DEVELOPMENT OF HIGH-LEVEL COMPUTER LANGUAGES

Bell Laboratories has designed a number of useful "high-level languages," sets of instructions that make it easier for people to use computers. One language can simulate the operation of an electrical circuit without the need to build an actual circuit model; another solves complicated algebraic problems; and others make it possible to control computer operations by English-language commands.

DEVELOPMENT OF PLATED-WIRE MEMORIES

The plated-wire memory uses the principle of the direction of magnetization in a material to store digital information. The original concept of the wire memory was invented in 1957 by U. F. Gianola of Bell Laboratories. Plated-wire memories require no standby power, are non-volatile, inexpensive to manufacture and will work in a high electrical noise environment.

DEVELOPMENT OF U. S. WW II RADAR

Bell Laboratories began research on radar in 1938 and during World War II designed about 100 different systems, including all fire-control radars on Navy ships. Major contributions were made to fire control and search radars—including the application of microwave frequencies to increase accuracy.

DEVELOPMENT OF AIR DEFENSE SYSTEMS

In 1945, the U. S. Government asked Bell Laboratories and Western Electric to develop a weapon system to defend against high-speed bombers. The result was the NIKE series—comprising surface-to-air missiles, radars, computers and guidance units—which ultimately evolved into the SAFEGUARD ballistic missile defense system.

DEVELOPMENT OF COMMAND GUIDANCE SYSTEM

The rockets that have launched 412 U. S. unmanned scientific space vehicles have been guided by Bell Laboratories' command guidance system. Conceived in 1954, it was developed for the U. S. Air Force's Titan I missile program and adopted in 1959 by NASA for many of their space vehicle boosters.

INVENTION OF CHIRP RADAR TECHNIQUES

The Chirp or pulse-compression technique for radar originated at Bell Labs in 1947. This technique, in which long, modulated pulses are transmitted and then compressed upon reception, permitted pulsed radar systems to have long range and high resolution while avoiding problems associated with generating and transmitting short pulses with high peak powers.

CONTRIBUTIONS TO OCEANOGRAPHIC RESEARCH

After World War II, Bell Laboratories was asked to assist with the nation's defense against submarines by developing techniques for gathering and analyzing information about acoustics in the ocean. The Laboratories' effort has resulted in sophisticated acoustic devices and data processing systems for better understanding the ocean environment and its effect on sound transmission. In addition, the Laboratories has made important contributions at a fundamental level to the science of ocean acoustics.

Appendix II

DATES IN CORPORATE HISTORY

1925 The Engineering Department of Western Electric (W.E.) was incorporated as Bell Telephone Laboratories at 463 West St., New York City. President: Frank B. Jewett. Staff: approximately 3600. Most of the staff worked in New York City, but there were two small field stations for radio research in Deal, N. J., and Cliffwood, N. J.

1926 Bell Laboratories acquired property in Whippany, N. J., where tests of high-power radio transmitters began. During and after World War II, Whippany was the center of Laboratories' work for the Department of Defense, and later for development of Bell System power supplies, transmission systems that connect customers to their central office, and other telephone equipment.

1928 Bell Laboratories acquired property in Chester, N. J., for a field station where engineers studied the effects of weather on telephone poles, wire and other outside plant apparatus. Chester became a separate laboratory in 1955 for development of construction methods and outside plant equipment and materials.

1930 Bell Laboratories opened a field station in Holmdel, N. J., where research on long-distance radio and waveguide transmission was carried on. In 1945 the groups at Holmdel were organized into a separate laboratory—called the Crawford Hill Laboratory—to continue this research. In 1962 a major Laboratories facility was added to the Holmdel tract. It housed exploratory development in switching, transmission and customer services; network planning; quality assurance; and, in 1966, the education center.

1930 A small group of Bell Laboratories engineers was assigned to the new Western Electric cable plant in Baltimore. In 1955 these groups were expanded, and the Baltimore Laboratory was formed to develop cables, wires, cords and related equipment for central offices and outside plant. In 1972 the Baltimore Laboratory was discontinued, and most of its operations were moved to a new Bell Laboratories-W.E. facility in Atlanta.

1934 The Development and Research Department of the American Telephone and Telegraph Company (AT&T) was consolidated with Bell Laboratories.

1940 Oliver E. Buckley succeeded Frank B. Jewett as president of Bell Laboratories.

1941 The first Bell Laboratories groups moved to the Murray Hill, N. J., Laboratory. Murray Hill later became corporate headquarters and the center for most research.

1946 In North Carolina, Bell Laboratories groups were assigned to work with Western Electric manufacturing organizations in Winston-Salem, Greensboro and Burlington. These groups furnished design information for manufacture of defense equipment. In 1950 they were organized as the North Carolina Laboratory, and in 1970 they were consolidated at a new facility called Guilford Center, where both Bell System and defense work is carried on.

1948 Bell Laboratories opened its first separate laboratory located with a Western Electric plant at W.E.'s electronic components plant in Allentown, Pa.—a move toward closer integration between Bell Laboratories design engineers and W.E. manufacturing groups.

1951 Mervin J. Kelly succeeded Oliver E. Buckley as president of Bell Laboratories.

1955 A laboratory for transmission systems development opened in Merrimack Valley, Mass., where Bell Laboratories groups design long-range coaxial cable, microwave radio relay, and other types of equipment for manufacture at the adjoining Western Electric plant.

1956 A new Western Electric plant in Indianapolis, Ind., became the home of another Bell Laboratories facility, where telephone sets and other customer-premises equipment are designed.

1958 At Western Electric's plant in Reading, Pa., a laboratory was formed to design electron tubes, and, later, semiconductor devices such as integrated circuits and light-emitting diodes (LED's).

1959 James B. Fisk succeeded Mervin J. Kelly as Bell Laboratories president.

1959 In a new Western Electric plant in Columbus, O., Bell Laboratories established a laboratory to design electromechanical switching systems for local and long-distance offices.

1966 The first major midwest laboratory opened at Indian Hill in Naperville, Ill., as a design center for electronic switching systems (ESS).

1966 As part of its efforts in developing ballistic missile defense systems, Bell Laboratories set up a facility on Kwajalein Atoll in the Marshall Islands of the Pacific Ocean. Engineers from the Laboratories, Western Electric and several subcontractors performed system tests of SAFEGUARD equipment.

1967 Bell Laboratories ended occupancy of its West Street laboratory in New York.

1969 Bell Laboratories opened a facility in Raritan River, N. J., with an adjunct at nearby Centennial Park, for work on Business Information Systems (BIS).

1969 A facility that houses AT&T, Western Electric and Bell Laboratories groups opened in Denver. Bell Laboratories personnel design private branch exchanges and key telephone equipment for business customers in close collaboration with AT&T marketing and W.E. manufacturing groups.

1971 Western Electric and Bell Laboratories began joint occupancy of a plant in Atlanta, Ga., where Laboratories groups design wire, cable and associated apparatus for W.E. to manufacture and purchase for the Bell System.

1971 A special computer facility for defense system development was set up by Bell Laboratories in Madison, N. J.

1973 William O. Baker succeeded James B. Fisk as Bell Laboratories president.

INDEX

*Denotes term in footnote or caption

control system 40
equalizer 175
intercept system 81
Message Accounting 85
Reporting on Trunks, Centralized 132
switches, step-by-step 87
translation 118
voice network 144
AUTOVON 144
Award, Outstanding Patent 161*

B

Bacon, F. 102
Bacon, W.M. 177
Baird, J. 134
Baker, W.O. iv,x,4,12,72,102,108,131,135,137,139,145,157*,181
Ballistic Missile Early Warning System 144
Baltimore Laboratory 180
Bandwidth, transmission 114
Banks, channel 101
Bardeen, J. 68*,69,93,172
Barium sodium niobate 105
Barium strontium niobate 105
Battery, solar 36*,44,72,73,172
Beck, A.C. 60
Bell Telephone Company, American 16*,25,26,158
Bell, A.G. 14*,15,28*,122*
Bell Laboratories Record 168*
Bell Labs News 158
Bell System Technical Journal 9,17*,49
Bellcomm, Inc. 146
Bennett, W.R. 171
Binary calculations 6*
BIS 181
BISCOM 133*
Black, H.S. 32,39-40,45,47,53,171-172
Blackboard, electronic 119*
BMEWS 144
Bobeck, A.H. 106,173
Bode, H.W. 3,31,32,53-4,174
Bombs, V-1 buzz 145*
Bonding, thermo-compression 73,96,173
Books written by Bell Laboratories authors 6
Bown, R. 5,60,61*,154
Boyle, W.S. 110,173
Brattain, W.H. 68*,69,93,172
Broadband
system 30*
telephone transmission 35,41

Broadcast radio receiver, superheterodyne 59
Broadcasting, high power 35
Brooks, H. 166
Bruce, E. 59,175
Bubble, magnetic 106,173
Buckhorn Mountain 57*
Buckley, O.E. 143,152,154*,180
Budget 160
Buehler, E. 73,172
Buildings, design of laboratory 10
Burr, I.W. 129
Business
information systems 181
information systems communications 133*
Buzz bombs, V-1 145*

C

Cable 42*,181
carrier system, underground 30
coaxial ix,32,35,52*
damage, undersea 41*
ocean 47,51*
sheathing 48,51
sheathing, polyethylene 175
splicing 139*
submarine 29
system, coaxial 37,53,175
telephone 48
transatlantic telephone 37,41*,176
underground 16
watertight 38*
Cabling assemblies 10
Calcium tungstate 105
Calculations, binary 6*
Calculator, Complex Number 110
Call
forwarding 81
waiting 81
Call Director telephone set 124*
Calls
alternate routing of 85
long distance 19
operator handled 86*
Call-a-matic telephone set 125*
Campbell, G.A. 16-18,20,23,26,31,34
Carbon contacts 19
Carbon dioxide laser 171
Card dialer, Touch-Tone 124*
Carnegie Institution of Washington 167
CAROT 132

*Denotes term in footnote or caption

*Denotes term in footnote or caption

*Denotes term in footnote or caption

*Denotes term in footnote or caption

*Denotes term in footnote or caption

*Denotes term in footnote or caption

*Denotes term in footnote or caption

Multiplexing 57*,175
Murray Hill Laboratory xi*,10,12*,104*,119*,169*,180
MUSA 60,175
M9 gun director 143,144,145*,178

N

NASA 38,71,119,146,179
National security 141
Nature
 of electrons, wave 6*
 of matter, wave 97-8,170
Negative
 feedback ix,6*,47,53,96
 feedback amplifier 32,45,171-172
 feedback circuit 39-40
Network
 analysis 128,137*
 automatic voice 144
 computer 115
 electrical 57
 monitoring 128
 Network Analysis and Feedback Amplifier Design 53
 operation and maintenance 10
 synthesis 175
 telephone 127
 theory 25,33,51,174-175
Networks and Feedback Systems, Symposium on Active 53*
New England Telephone Company 14*
New York, Economic Club of 94*
NIKE 179
 Ajax system 148*
 Antiaircraft missiles 144
Nobel Prize 68*,95,97,161*,170,172
Noise 25
 effect, thermal 45
 Johnson 103
 star 59,108
 theory 32,175
 thermal 96,103,107,171
 white 103
Nondecimal dialing 88
Number Calculator, Complex 110
Numbering plan 85
Nyquist criterion 45
Nyquist diagram 53
Nyquist, H. 31,32,35,45-6,53,174

O

O'Neill, E. 55,66
Ocean

acoustics 179
 cable 45,51*
Oceanographic research 179
Office, electronic central 80
Operating
 system, computer 178
 system, time-shared 178
Operations research 131
Operator-handled calls 86*
Optical
 communication system ix,55,157*
 fiber vi*,41,105,120*
 transmission ix,101,173
Orientation program, INTRO 8,162*
Oscillator, crystal 58
Oscillograph, cathode-ray 103*
Outside plant 180
Outstanding Patent Award 161*
Over-the-horizon
 microwave transmission 147*
 system 37
Overseas radiotelephony 29,35,175
Oxide masking 96,172

P

Pacific Telephone and Telegraph Company 31*
Panama-Pacific Exposition 152
Panel
 switching system 90
 telephone set 125*
Parametric amplifier 174
Parkinson, D.B. 178
Patel, C.K.N. 167*,171
Patent 34*,160*
 Award, Outstanding 161*
PBX 77*,136*,161,181
PCM 42,78,176
Pearson, G.L. 73,172,174
People's Republic of China 9*
Peoples, R. 138
Perimeter Acquisition Radar 149*
Permalloy 51
Pfann, W.G. 73,172
Pfannstiehl, A.S. 99*
Phantom circuit 19
Phone, wristwatch 55
Photoelectric effect 114
Pictures, sound motion 99*,117,170
Picturephone 7,37,42,50,52,101,124,177
Pierce, J.R. 49,60,66*,71-2,83*,148*,174,175

*Denotes term in footnote or caption

*Denotes term in footnote or caption

*Denotes term in footnote or caption

*Denotes term in footnote or caption

*Denotes term in footnote or caption

*Denotes term in footnote or caption

*Denotes term in footnote or caption